The Gig Book

101 Hits

Published by
Wise Publications
14-15 Berners Street,
London W1T 3LJ, UK.

Exclusive Distributors:
Music Sales Limited
Distribution Centre,
Newmarket Road, Bury St Edmunds,
Suffolk IP33 3YB, UK.
Music Sales Pty Limited
20 Resolution Drive, Caringbah,
NSW 2229, Australia.

Order No. AM997524
ISBN 978-1-84938-094-2

Compiled by Nick Crispin.
Text by Graham Vickers.
Picture research by Jacqui Black.
Photographs courtesy of;
LFI - 21, 151.
Getty - 61, 73, 93, 109, 181, 225 & 253.
Rex Features - 5.
Music engraved by Paul Ewers Music Design.
Edited by Tom Farncombe and Adrian Hopkins.
Design by Fresh Lemon.

www.musicsales.com

Printed in Thailand.

Wise Publications
part of The Music Sales Group
London/New York/Paris/Sydney/Copenhagen/Berlin/Tokyo/Madrid

Introduction 4

A Girl Like You –
Edwyn Collins................................ 6

Ain't Nobody –
Rufus & Chaka Khan....................... 8

Alive – Pearl Jam........................... 10

All Out Of Love – Air Supply 16

All That She Wants –
Ace Of Bass.................................... 13

Alone Again Or – Love 18

Baker Street –
Gerry Rafferty 22

Band On The Run – Wings......... 24

The Boxer –
Simon & Garfunkel 28

Brothers In Arms –
Dire Straits 33

Born Free – Matt Monro............. 32

Call Me – Blondie 36

Clocks – Coldplay 39

Common People – Pulp 42

Could It Be Magic? –
Barry Manilow 45

Cry Me A River –
Justin Timberlake......................... 48

Downtown – Petula Clark 52

Dreams – Fleetwood Mac........... 55

Drive – The Cars........................... 58

Ever Fallen In Love
(With Someone You
Shouldn't've) – Buzzcocks........... 62

End Of The Road –
Boyz II Men 64

Englishman In New York –
Sting... 67

Everything Must Go –
Manic Street Preachers............... 70

God Only Knows –
The Beach Boys 74

Goldfinger – Shirley Bassey 76

Gotta Get Thru This –
Daniel Bedingfield 78

Graceland – Paul Simon 80

Have I Told You Lately –
Van Morrison................................. 84

He Ain't Heavy, He's My
Brother – The Hollies................... 86

Heaven – Bryan Adams............... 90

Here Comes The Rain Again –
Eurythmics 88

Hit The Road Jack –
Ray Charles 94

Hold On – KT Tunstall 97

Hot Fun In The Summertime –
Sly And The Family Stone....... 106

How Soon Is Now? –
The Smiths 100

Human Nature –
Michael Jackson.......................... 102

I Got You (I Feel Good) –
James Brown 110

I Touch Myself –
The Divinyls 112

I'd Like To Teach The World
To Sing – The New Seekers..... 118

I'm Outta Love –
Anastacia...................................... 115

In Between Days –
The Cure 120

It Must Be Love – Madness 126

It's A Sin – Pet Shop Boys........ 123

It's Not Unusual –
Tom Jones 128

(I've Had) The Time Of
My Life – Bill Medley
& Jennifer Warnes 131

Jailbreak – Thin Lizzy 134

Just The Two Of Us –
Bill Withers.................................. 138

Le Freak – Chic 136

Life On Mars? –
David Bowie 144

Like A Virgin – Madonna 146

Little Red Corvette –
Prince 139

Love Is In The Air –
John Paul Young 148

Love Will Tear Us Apart –
Joy Division 152

Massachusetts –
The Bee Gees 153

The Model – Kraftwerk 154

Move Over Darling –
Doris Day 156

Mr. Brightside – The Killers... 159

Once In A Lifetime –
Talking Heads 162

One More Night –
Phil Collins 166

Only The Lonely –
Roy Orbison 169

Prince Charming –
Adam And The Ants 170

Put Your Records On –
Corinne Bailey Rae 172

Rasputin – Boney M 174

Rave On – Buddy Holly 178

Real Wild Child
(Wild One) – Iggy Pop 176

Respect – Aretha Franklin 182

Rock Your Baby –
George McCrae 184

Roll With It – Oasis 185

S.O.S. – ABBA 188

Sailing – Rod Stewart 190

She's Not There –
The Zombies 194

She's The One –
Robbie Williams 191

Somewhere Only We Know –
Keane 196

Son Of A Preacher Man –
Dusty Springfield 200

Stand By Me –
Ben E. King 207

Summer In The City –
Lovin' Spoonful 208

Sweet Caroline –
Neil Diamond 203

There She Goes –
The La's 210

This Love – Maroon 5 212

Time After Time –
Cyndi Lauper 214

Tired Of Being Alone –
Al Green 217

Try A Little Tenderness –
Otis Redding 218

Turn It On Again –
Genesis 221

Twist And Shout –
The Beatles 226

Up The Junction –
Squeeze 229

Up Where We Belong –
Jennifer Warnes &
Joe Cocker 232

Vienna – Ultravox 234

Virginia Plain –
Roxy Music 236

Waiting In Vain –
Bob Marley 238

Wake Up Little Susie –
Everly Brothers 244

Walk On By –
Dionne Warwick 241

Way Down – Elvis Presley 246

We Are Family –
Sister Sledge 248

What's Love Got To Do
With It – Tina Turner 250

Why Does It Always Rain
On Me? – Travis 257

With Or Without You – U2 254

You Do Something To Me –
Paul Weller 270

You Never Can Tell –
Chuck Berry 260

Your Song – Elton John 262

You're Gorgeous –
Babybird 266

You're So Vain –
Carly Simon 268

Introduction

The 101 Hits GigBook is pretty much guaranteed to contain a generous helping of your all-time favourite numbers.

From the fifties to the noughties, here are the songs that made the charts in the UK, the US and sometimes around the world. Fifties fans can strum and sing to the ever-fresh hits of The Everly Brothers and Buddy Holly after which pretty much every pop genre gets represented. You'll have your own favourites, but some are undisputed classics. Chuck Berry's wedding narrative song 'You Never Can Tell' has appealed to many performers over the years including Bruce Springsteen, Emmylou Harris, John Prine and even Mary Elizabeth Mastrantonio who, in her role as a low-rent bar singer, sang it in John Sayles' movie *Limbo*. Paul Simon's 'Graceland' was perhaps the high spot of his solo career while the same might be said for 'It's Not Unusual' and Tom Jones. Dire Straits 'Brothers In Arms' was the title song from what became the first ever big-selling CD album while 'A Girl Like You' was the high visibility hit that almost

became a requiem for the Scottish singer Edwyn Collins, pictured right, who slowly recovered from the devastating illness that almost killed him. Pulp's 'Common People' appears in all its bitter vernacular glory and so does Carly Simon's 'You're So Vain' with its eternal built-in guessing game as to the identity of the self-absorbed lover in question… Mick Jagger? Warren Beatty? Or Yusuf Islam, as he prefers to be known these days? Songs made famous by everyone from Michael Jackson and The Pet Shop Boys to Babybird and Keane are also included… proof that there is something for everybody here. That said, if you're itching to start playing and singing Aretha Franklin's 'Respect' you may be in no hurry to tackle Doris Day's 'Move Over Darling'… but then that was always the charm of the charts: if enough people bought it, the song was a hit. Here are 101 that fit the bill. Play, sing and enjoy.

A Girl Like You

Words & Music by Edwyn Collins

♩ = 136

1. I've nev-er known a girl like you be-fore,   now
(Verse 2 see block lyrics)

just like in a song from days   of yore,

hear you come a' knock-in' knock-in' on   my door,__   and I've

nev-er met a girl like   you   be-fore.__   (2. Now)
(3. You've)

made me ac-know-ledge   the   de-vil in me,__   I'll hope to God I'm talk-in' me-ta-

-pho-ri-cally,__   hope that I'm talk-ing al-le-go-ri-cally,__

6

know that I'm talk-in' 'bout the way I feel,___ and I've nev-er met a girl like

you be-fore.   Nev-er,   nev-er,   nev-er,   nev-er,

nev-er met a girl like   you be-fore.   This old town's changed so much,

don't feel like   I   be-long,___   too ma-ny   pro-test   sing-ers,

not   e-nough   pro-test   songs___ and now you've come a-long,   yes

you've come a-long,   and I've nev-er met a girl like   you be-fore.___

Verse 2:
Now give me just a taste so I want more
Now my hands are bleeding and my knees are raw
Now you've got me crawlin' crawlin' on the floor
And I've never known a girl like you before.

Ain't Nobody

Words & Music by David Wolinski

(Original key E♭ minor. To match original recording tune guitar down one semitone)

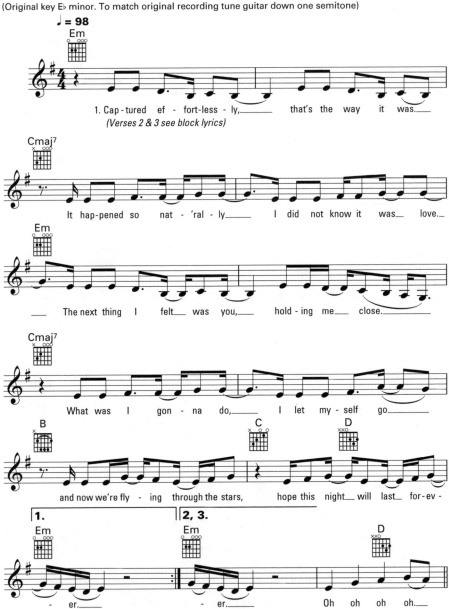

♩ = 98

Em
1. Cap - tured ef - fort - less - ly,_____ that's the way it was.___
(Verses 2 & 3 see block lyrics)

Cmaj7
It hap-pened so nat - 'ral - ly_____ I did not know it was___ love.___

Em
___ The next thing I felt___ was you,_____ hold - ing me___ close.___

Cmaj7
What was I gon - na do,_____ I let my - self go___

B   **C**   **D**
and now we're fly - ing through the stars, hope this night___ will last___ for-ev -

1.
Em
- er._____

2, 3.
Em   **D**
- er._____ Oh oh oh oh.___

8

Ain't no-bo-dy loves me bet-ter, makes me hap-py, makes me feel this__ way.

Ain't no-bo-dy loves me bet-ter__ than you.

At first you put____ your arms____ a-round me,
I can't re-sist____ this sweet sur-ren-der,
We stare____ in-to____ each oth-er's eyes,

Play 3 times

then__ you put your charms a-round me, I've got__
oh, my nights are warm and__ ten-der.
and what we see is no__ su-prise.

D.S. *(repeat chorus) to fade*

—— a feel-ing most would trea-sure, and a love so deep we can-not mea-sure.

Verse 2:
I've been waiting for you
It's been so long
I knew just what I would do
When I heard your song
You filled my heart with a kiss
You gave me freedom
You knew I could not resist
I needed someone
And now we're flying through the stars
And hope this night will last forever.

Verse 3:
I wait for night time to come
To bring you to me
I can't believe I'm the one
I was so lonely
I feel like no one before
I must be dreaming
I want this dream to be real
I need this feeling
I make my wish upon a star
And hope this night will last forever.

Alive

Words by Eddie Vedder • Music by Stone Gossard

1."Son," _____ she said, "Have I got a lit-tle sto-ry for you,_
(Verse 2 see block lyrics)

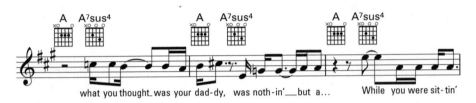

what you thought was your dad-dy, was noth-in'_but a... While you were sit-tin'

home a-lone at age_thir-teen, your real dad-dy was dy - in'. Sor-ry you did-n't_

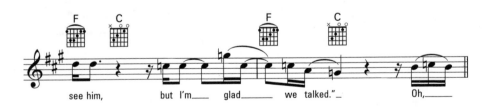

see him, but I'm_ glad_____ we talked."_ Oh,_

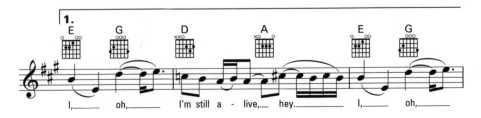

I,_ oh,_ I'm still a - live,_ hey._ I,_ oh,_

11

Verse 2:
While she walks slowly across a young man's room
She said: "I'm ready for you."
I can't remember anything to this very day
Except the love, the love
Oh, you know where, now I can see, I just stare.

All That She Wants

Words & Music by Buddha & Joker

♩ = 94

She leads a lone - ly___ life.___

She leads a lone - ly__ life.___

Well, she woke up late in the morn-ing light   and the

day had just be - gun._____   She o-pened up her eyes_ and thought,

"Oh, what a morn - ing."   It's not a day for work,___   it's a

day for catch-ing tan, just ly-ing on the beach_ and hav-ing fun._

_ She's going to get_ ya. All_ that she wants_ is_ an-oth-er

ba-by. She's gone to-mor-row, boy, all_ that she wants_ is_ an-oth-er

ba-by, yeah._ All_ that she wants_ is_ an-oth-er

ba-by. She's gone to-mor-row, boy, all_ that she wants_ is_ an-oth-er

ba-by, yeah._

1.

All that she wants.

14

All Out Of Love

Words & Music by Graham Russell & Clive Davis

Verse 2:
I wish I could carry your smile in my heart
For times when my life seems so low
It would make me believe what tomorrow could bring
When today doesn't really know, doesn't really know.

Verse 3:
I want you to come back and carry me home
Away from these long, lonely nights
I'm reaching for you. Are you feeling it too?
Does the feeling seem oh, so right?

Verse 4:
And what would you say if I called on you now
And said that I can't hold on?
There's no easy way, it gets harder each day
Please love me or I'll be gone.

Alone Again Or

Words & Music by Brian MacLean

19

Baker Street

Previously mainly famous as the address of a fictional Victorian detective, London's Baker Street achieved new recognition in 1978, even if it was depicted as something of a boulevard of broken dreams by Gerry Rafferty. The singer's successful bid for chart independence following the acrimonious dissolution of Stealer's Wheel came from his second solo album, *City To City*. 'Baker Street' reached No. 3 in the UK and No. 2 in the US. Good as the song was, the cherry on top was Raphael Ravenscroft's eight-bar saxophone solo that became so popular, it single-handedly revived the fortunes of the instrument for a time.

Gerry Rafferty

Baker Street

Words & Music by Gerry Rafferty

1. Wind-ing your way down Bak - er Street,
(Verse 2 see block lyrics)

light in your head and_ dead_ on your feet, well an - oth - er craz-y day,_ you

drink the night a - way_ and for - get a-bout ev - 'ry - thing._

This ci - ty de-sert makes you feel so cold,_ it's got so ma-ny peo-ple but it's

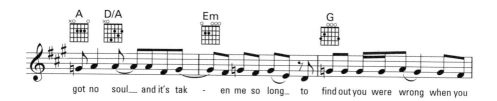

got no soul__ and it's tak - en me so long__ to find out you were wrong when you

sor-ted out ev - 'ry - thing.____ You used to think that it was so ea - sy,

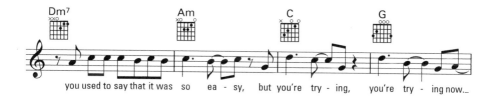

you used to say that it was so ea - sy, but you're try - ing, you're try - ing now.__

__ An-oth-er year and then you'll be hap - py, just one more year and then you'll

be hap - py, but you're cry - ing, you're cry - ing now.____

Verse 2:

Way down the street there's a lad in his place
He opens the door, he's got that look on his face
And he asks you where you've been
You tell him who you've seen and you talk about anything
He's got this dream about buying some land
He's gonna give up the booze and the one-night stands
And then he'll settle down in some quiet little town
And forget about everything.

But you know he'll always keep moving
You know he's never gonna stop moving
'Cause he's the rolling
He's a rolling stone
And when you wake up it's a new morning
The sun is shining, it's a new morning
And you're going
You're going home.

23

Band On The Run

Words & Music by Paul McCartney & Linda McCartney

♩ = 82

1. Stuck in-side these four walls,___ sent in-side for-ev - er,___
nev - er see-ing no one___ nice a - gain,___ like
you,___ ma - ma, you,___
ma - ma, you.___

(Synth 2ª)

2. If I ev-er get out___ of here thought of giv-ing it all___ a - way

to a reg-is-tered char - i - ty. All I need is a pint__ a day if I

ev-er get out__ of here.__ (If we ev-er get out__ of here.)__

♩ = 126

(Gtr.)

3. Well, the rain ex - plod - ed with a might-y crash, as we fell in - to__ the sun,
(Verses 4, 5. see block lyrics)

and the first one said to the sec-ond one there,__ I

hope you're hav-ing fun._____ Band on the run,__

25

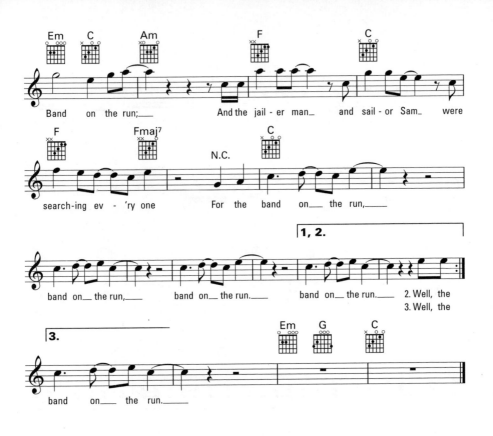

Band on the run;___ And the jail-er man_ and sail-or Sam_ were

search-ing ev - 'ry one For the band on___ the run,___

1, 2.

band on___ the run,___ band on___ the run.___ band on___ the run.___ 2. Well, the
3. Well, the

3.

band on___ the run.___

Verse 4:
Well the undertaker drew a heavy sigh
Seeing no one else had come
And a bell was ringing in the village square
For the rabbits on the run.

Band on the run, band on the run.
And the jailer man and sailor Sam
Were searching ev'ryone
For the band on the run, band on the run
Band on the run, band on the run.

Verse 5:
Well the night was falling as the desert world
Began to settle down
In the town they're searching for us ev'rywhere
But we never will be found.

Band on the run, band on the run
And the county judge who held a grudge
Will search for ever more
For the band on the run, band on the run
Band on the run, band on the run.

26

The Boxer

'The Boxer' was a 1969 hit for Simon & Garfunkel taken from their *Bridge Over Troubled Water* album. It told the bleak and symbolic story of a young boxer far from home, exploited and brutalised by the business he's in, thinking of quitting and knowing he can't. One of the song's original verses was omitted from the recording — perhaps surprisingly *not* the one that mentions taking comfort from the whores on Seventh Avenue. Even so, leaving that reference in didn't seem to harm the song's radio plays, although some versions of this much-covered song substituted 'girls' for 'whores', perhaps in the hope that non-New Yorkers might believe the comfort-givers to be nuns or social workers. Anyway, the song had instant classic written all over it. Subsequently even Bob Dylan and Neil Diamond recorded it and, forty years on, it still features in most all-time top song lists.

The Boxer

Words & Music by Paul Simon

29

li, la, li,_____ li, li, la, li._____ Li, la, li,___

li, la, li,_____ li, li, la, li,_____ la, la, la, la,

To Coda ⊕

li.

3. Ask - ing on -

4. And I'm lay-

- ing out____ my win - ter clothes____ and wish - ing I____ was

gone, go - in' home.____ Where the New York Ci - ty

win - ters are - n't bleed - ing me, lead - ing

30

Verse 3:
Asking only workman's wages
I come looking for a job, but I get no offers
Just a come-on from the whores on Seventh Avenue
I do declare, there were times when I was so lonesome
I took some comfort there.
La, la, la, la, la, la, la.

Verse 5:
In the clearing stands a boxer, and a fighter by his trade
And he carries the reminders of every glove that laid him down
Or cut him till he cried out in his anger and his shame
I am leaving, I am leaving, but the fighter still remains.

31

Born Free

Words by Don Black • Music by John Barry

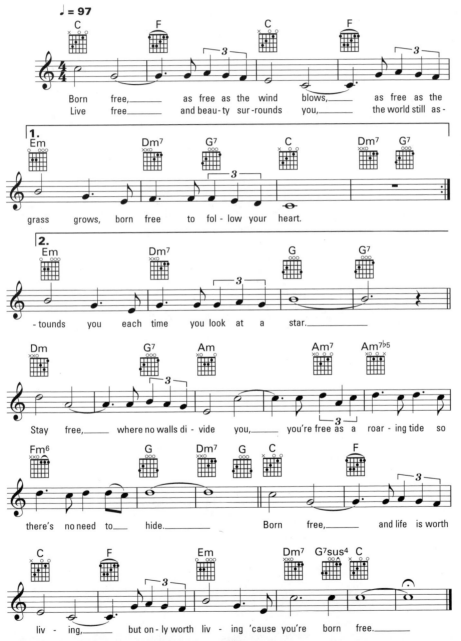

Born free, as free as the wind blows, as free as the
Live free and beau-ty sur-rounds you, the world still as -

1.
grass grows, born free to fol - low your heart.

2.
- tounds you each time you look at a star.

Stay free, where no walls di - vide you, you're free as a roar - ing tide so

there's no need to hide. Born free, and life is worth

liv - ing, but on - ly worth liv - ing 'cause you're born free.

Brothers In Arms

Words & Music by Mark Knopfler

1. These mist co-vered moun - tains___

are a home now for me, but my home is the low-

- lands___ and al - ways will be.

Some-day you'll re - turn___ to___ your val-leys and your

farms, and you'll no lon - ger burn to___ be bro - thers_ in arms___

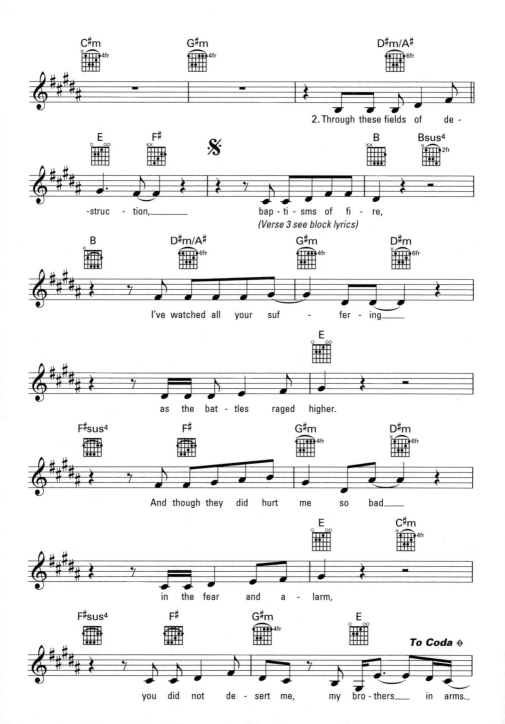

2. Through these fields of de- -struc - tion,_____ bap - ti - sms of fi - re,

(Verse 3 see block lyrics)

I've watched all your suf - fer - ing_____ as the bat - tles raged higher. And though they did hurt me so bad_____ in the fear and a - larm, you did not de - sert me, my bro - thers_____ in arms._____

To Coda ⊕

Verse 2:
Now the sun's gone to hell and the moon's riding high
Let me bid you farewell, ev'ry man has to die
But it's written in the starlight and ev'ry line on your palm
We're fools to make war on our brothers in arms.

Call Me

Words & Music by Giorgio Moroder & Deborah Harry

♩ = 142

Col-our me___ your col - our, ba - by, col-our me___ your car.___

Col-our me___ your col - our, darl - ing, I know who___ you are.___

Come up off___ your col - our chart, I know where_you're com - ing from. Call me___

___ on the line, call me, call me an - y, an - y - time,___ call me,

___ I love you, can't you call me an - y day___ or night.___ Call

me! *Instrumental*

Clocks

Words & Music by Guy Berryman, Chris Martin, Jon Buckland & Will Champion

Capo 1st fret ♩ = **130**

1. The lights go out and I can't be saved, tides that I tried to
(Verse 2 see block lyrics)

swim a - gainst, have brought me down up - on my knees, oh, I beg, I

beg and plead. Sing - ing; come out with things un - said.__ Shoot, an ap - ple

off my head.__ And a trou - ble that can't be named. A ti - ger's wait - ing

to be tamed. Sing - ing... You_____ are.__

___ You_____ are.__

com - pares._____

You_____ are.___ You_____

___ are.___ Home, home___ where I want - ed to go.

Piano

Repeat ad lib. to fade

Verse 2:
Confusion that never stops
The closing doors and the ticking clocks
Gonna come back and take you home
I could not stop that you now know
Singing… come out upon my seas
Cursed missed opportunities
Am I a part of the cure
Or am I part of the disease?
Singing…

Common People

Words by Jarvis Cocker

Music by Jarvis Cocker, Nick Banks, Russell Senior, Candida Doyle & Stephen Mackey

♩ = 142

1. She came from Greece she had a thirst for know - ledge, she stud-ied sculp-ture at Saint

(Verse 2 see block lyrics)

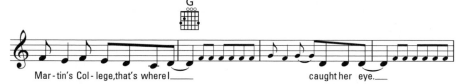

Mar - tin's Col - lege, that's where I_____ caught her eye._

She told me that her dad was load - ed, I said "In that case I'll have rum and

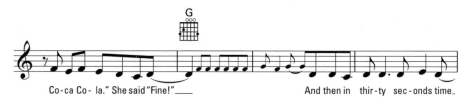

Co-ca Co - la." She said "Fine!"_____ And then in thir-ty sec-onds time_

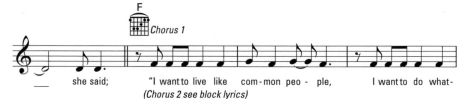

Chorus 1

_ she said; "I want to live like com-mon peo - ple, I want to do what-

(Chorus 2 see block lyrics)

- ev-er com-mon peo-ple do.___ Want to sleep with com-mon peo - ple, I want to sleep with

com-mon peo-ple like you.___ What else could I do?"___ I said

"I'll see what I can do." ___ She just smiled and held_ my hand.___

(Guitar solo 2nd time)

___ Rent a flat___ a-bove a shop,___ cut your hair___ and get_ a job,___ smoke some fags___

___and play_some pool,___ pre-tend you nev - er went to school.___ But still you'll nev -

- er get_ it right,___ 'cause when you're laid___ in bed_ at night__ watch-ing roach-

- es climb the wall,___ if you called_your dad_ he could stop___ it all,___yeah!

Chorus 3

You'll nev-er live like com-mon peo-ple,___ you'll nev-er do what - ev-er com-mon peo-ple do,___
(Chorus 4 see block lyrics)

43

nev-er fail like com-mon peo - ple, you'll nev-er watch your life___ slide out of view,___

___and dance___ and drink and screw,___ be-cause there's noth - ing else to do.

Play 6 times

___ Want to live with com-mon peo - ple like you,

want to live with com-mon peo - ple like you.___ La___ la la___ la,

Oh!___ La___ la la___ la, Ooh!___ La___ la la la la, oh you!

Verse 2:
I took her down to a supermarket
I don't know why, but I had to start it somewhere
So it started there
I said "Pretend you've got no money."
But she just laughed and said "Oh you're so funny!"
I said "Yeah?"
(Spoken) "Well, I can't see anyone else smiling in here."

Chorus 2:
"Are you sure you want to live like common people?"
You want to see whatever common people see
Want to sleep with common people
You want to sleep with common people like me
But she didn't understand
She just smiled and held my hand.

Chorus 4:
Sing along with the common people
Sing along and it might just get you through
Laugh along with the common people
Laugh along even though they're laughing at you
And the stupid things that you do
Because you think that poor is cool.

44

Could It Be Magic

Words & Music by Barry Manilow & Adrienne Anderson

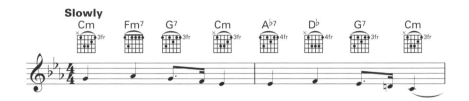

An - gel of___ my life - time, an - swer to___ all an -

- swers I can find; Ba - by I love__ you.

Come, come, come in - to___ my__

(2° see block lyrics)

arms. Let me know__ the won - der of

To Coda ⊕ **1.** **2.**

all__ of you.__ Ba - by I want_ you.

46

D.S. al Coda

Coda

| G7/F | Cm/Eb | G/D | Cm | Ab/C |

Could it be mag - ic? Come, come,
(2° see block lyrics)

| Gmaj9/B | G/B | Bbmaj7 | Bb6 | Am7 |

come in - to____ my____ arms. Let me know___ the won -

1, 2. **3.**

| Ab7 | Gsus4 | G | G7/F | Cm/Eb | G/D | G | Cm | Em |

- der of all___ of you___ Ba - by I want you.

| G7 | Cm | Ab | Db | G7aug | G7 | Cm |

Verse 2:
Lady take me high upon a hillside
High up where the stallion meets the sun
I could love you
Building my world around you
Never leave you till my life is done
Baby I love you.

2°
Now, now, now and hold on fast
Could this be the magic at last.

47

Cry Me A River

Words & Music by Justin Timberlake, Scott Storch & Tim Mosley

- er girl. Cry me a riv - er, cry me a riv-

1. **2.**

- er girl. Cry me a riv - - er girl. Cry me a riv -
(Yeah, yeah.)

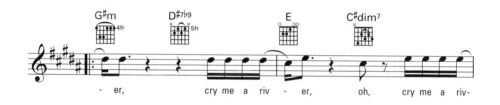

- er, cry me a riv - er, oh, cry me a riv-

Repeat ad lib. to fade

- er. Oh, cry me a riv - er. Oh, cry me a riv-

Verse 2:
I know that they say that some things are better left unsaid
It wasn't like you only talked to him and you know it
(Don't act like you don't know it)
All of those things people told me keep messing with my head
You should've picked honesty then you may not have blown it.

Downtown

Words & Music by Tony Hatch

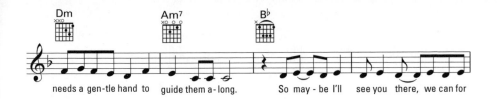

needs a gen-tle hand to guide them a-long. So may-be I'll see you there, we can for

-get all our trou-bles, for - get all our cares. So go down - town, things-'ll be great when you're

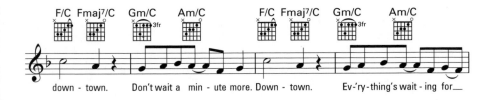

down - town. Don't wait a min - ute more. Down - town. Ev-'ry-thing's wait - ing for—

Repeat ad lib. to fade

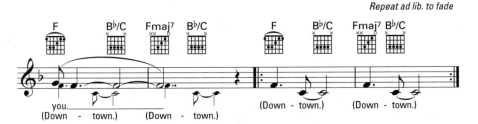

you._____ (Down - town.) (Down - town.)
(Down - town.) (Down - town.)

Verse 2:
Don't hang around and let your problems surround you
There are movie shows downtown
Maybe you know some little places to go to
Where they never close, downtown
Just listen to the rhythm of a gentle bossanova
You'll be dancing with them too
Before the night is over, happy again
The lights are much brighter there
You can forget all your troubles
Forget all your cares.

So go downtown where all the lights are bright
Downtown, waiting for you tonight
Downtown, you're gonna be all right now.

54

Dreams

Words & Music by Stevie Nicks

thun - der on - ly hap - pens_ when it's rain - ing,

play-ers on - ly love_____ you_ when they're play - ing._____ Say,_

wo - men, they will come_____ and_ they will go._____

When the rain_ wash - es_____ you clean you'll know,_____ you'll

know,_____ you will_ know. Oh,_____ oh,_ oh,_ you'll know.

Verse 2:
Now here I go again, I see the crystal vision
I keep my visions to myself
It's only me who want to wrap around your dreams
And have you any dreams you'd like to sell?
Dreams of loneliness.

Drive

Words & Music by Ric Ocasek

Capo 2nd fret   ♩ = **84**

1. Who's gon-na tell you when__ it's__ too__ late?
(Verse 4 see block lyrics)

Who's gon-na tell you things__ aren't__ so__ great?

You can't go on__ think-ing no-thing's wrong,

__ oh no.__ Who's gon-na drive you home__ to-night?__

To Coda ⊕

2. Who's gon-na pick you up__ when you__ fall?_
(Verse 3 see block lyrics)

Who's gon-na hang it up__ when you__ call?

Verse 3:
Who's gonna pay attention to your dreams?
Who's gonna plug your ears when you scream?

Verse 4:
Who's gonna hold you down when you shake?
Who's gonna come around when you break?

Ever Fallen In Love (With Someone You Shouldn't've)

Fans of Buzzcocks often see their heroes as exemplars of punk's raw in-your-face originality, so it is somehow rather disarming to discover that the band's Pete Shelley took inspiration from a line of dialogue in the cosy 1955 movie version of *Guys And Dolls* when he wrote 'Ever Fallen in Love (With Someone You Shouldn't've)'. The song certainly proved to have legs, later providing a minor hit for Fine Young Cannibals and more recently being covered by The Stiff Dylans who reprised it for the 2008 movie *Angus, Thongs And Perfect Snogging*. It also was the choice of song for a charity single launched in John Peel's memory for the benefit of Amnesty International. That celebrity-heavy version featured Roger Daltrey, The Futureheads, Elton John, Robert Plant and composer Pete Shelley among others.

Buzzcocks

Ever Fallen In Love
(With Someone You Shouldn't've)

Words & Music by Pete Shelley

♩ = 142

1. You spurn my nat-ural em-o - tions, you make me feel like dirt__

(Verses 2 & 3 see block lyrics)

_____ and that hurts.____ And

if I start a com-mo - tion, I run the risk of los - ing you____ and that's worse.__

____ Ev - er fall in love_ with some - one ev-er fal-len in love_

____ in love with some - one, ev-er fal-len in love,____ in love with some- one

____ you shouldn't-'ve fal-len in love__ with?   2. I   3. You dis -

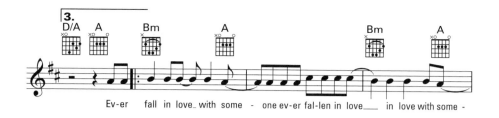

Ev-er fall in love_ with some - one ev-er fal-len in love___ in love with some -

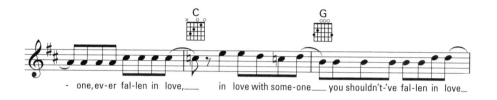

- one, ev-er fal-len in love,___ in love with some-one___ you shouldn't-'ve fal-len in love_

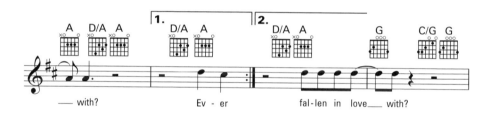

— with?   Ev - er   fal-len in love___ with?

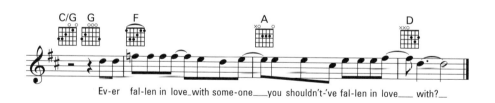

Ev-er fal-len in love_with some-one___you shouldn't-'ve fal-len in love___ with?_

Verse 2:
I can't see much of a future
Unless we find out what's to blame; what a shame
And we won't be together much longer
Unless we realise that we are the same.

Verse 3:
You disturb my natural emotions
You make me feel like dirt and that hurts
And if I start a commotion
I'll only end up losing you and that's worse.

End Of The Road

Words & Music by Kenny Edmonds, Antonio Reid & Daryl Simmons

♪ = 149

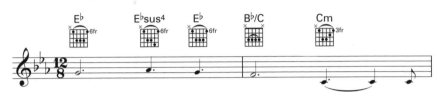

(Spoken) Girl, you know we belong together;   I don't have no time

for you to be playin' with my heart like this.   You'll be mine forever, baby, you just see.

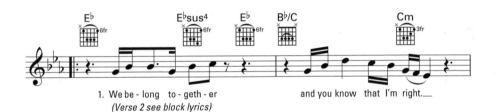

1. We be - long to - geth - er   and you know that I'm right.___
(Verse 2 see block lyrics)

Why do you play with my heart? Why do you play with my mind?___

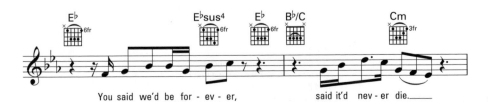

You said we'd be for - ev - er,   said it'd nev - er die.___

How could you love me and leave me and nev-er say good-bye? Well, I

can't sleep at night with-out hold-ing you tight. Girl, each time I try I just break down and cry.

Pain in my head, oh, I'd rath-er be dead,___ spin-nin' a-round and a-round. Al-though we've

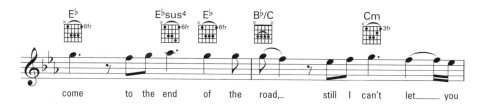

come to the end of the road,___ still I can't let___ you

go.___ It's un-na-tu-ral. You be-long to me, I be-long to you.___

Come to the end of the road,___ still I can't let___ you

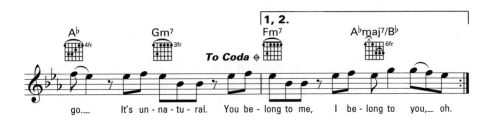

go.— It's un-na-tu-ral. You be-long to me, I be-long to you,— oh.

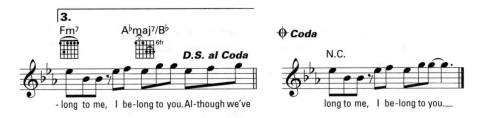

- long to me, I be-long to you. Al-though we've   long to me, I be-long to you.—

Verse 2:
Girl, I know you really love me
You just don't realize
You've never been there before
It's only your first time
Maybe I'll forgive you
Maybe you'll try
We should be happy together
Forever you and I
Could you love me again like you loved me before?
This time I want you to love me much more
This time instead, just come to my bed
And, baby, just don't let me down.

Verse 3:
(Spoken:)
Girl, I'm here for you
All those times at night when you just hurt me
And just ran out with that other fellow
Baby, I knew about it
I just didn't care
You just don't understand how much I love you, do you?
I'm here for you
I'm not out to go out there and cheat all night just like you did, baby
But that's alright, huh, I love you anyway
And I'm still gonna be here for you 'til my dyin' day, baby
Right now, I'm just in so much pain, baby
'Cause you just won't come back to me, will you?
Just come back to me.
Yes, baby, my heart is lonely
My heart hurts, baby, yes, I feel pain too
Baby please...

Englishman In New York

Words & Music by Sting

67

Verse 3:
If "Manners maketh man," as someone said
He's the hero of the day
It takes a man to suffer ignorance and smile
Be yourself no matter what they say.

Verse 4:
Takes more than combat gear to make a man
Takes more than a licence for a gun
Confront your enemies, avoid them when you can
A gentleman will walk but never run.

Verse 5:
If "Manners maketh man," as someone said
He's the hero of the day
It takes a man to suffer ignorance and smile
Be yourself no matter what they say.

Everything Must Go

Words by Nicky Wire • Music by James Bradfield & Sean Moore

Verse 2:
I look to the future, it makes me cry
But it seems too real to tell you why
Freed from the century, with nothing
But memory, memory.

God Only Knows

A monumental pop construct, 'God Only Knows' is inseparable from The Beach Boys' dramatic recording of it. Released in the summer of 1966 the record banished any lingering doubts that the Southern Californian quintet (pictured here with bandmate Bruce Johnston) was aiming to achieve immortality. With its nods to everybody from Richard Wagner to The Lovin' Spoonful, and a 20-odd army of musicians playing woodwind, strings, accordion, bass, guitars, drums and more, the song represented a thinly-disguised bid for glory that co-writer Brian Wilson has been happy to embellish in recent years. Paul McCartney has made no secret of the fact that he believes 'God Only Knows' is "a really, really great song — it's a big favourite of mine. It's very deep. Very emotional, always a bit of a choker for me". It was co-written by Tony Asher and his opening line — 'I may not always love you' — was initially resisted by Wilson as being a bit feeble for a love song, but Asher fought for it and it stayed.

The Beach Boys

God Only Knows

Words & Music by Brian Wilson & Tony Asher

Verse 2:
If you should ever leave me
Though life would still go on, believe me
The world could show nothing to me
So what good would living do me?

Goldfinger

Words by Leslie Bricusse & Anthony Newley • Music by John Barry

Gotta Get Thru This

Words & Music by Daniel Bedingfield

Graceland

Words & Music by Paul Simon

♩ = 120

1. The Mis-sis-sip-pi Del-ta__ was shin-ing like a na-tion-al gui-tar.__

__ I am fol-low-ing__ the riv-er down__ the high-

-way through the cra-dle of the civ-il war. I'm go-ing to Grace-

-land, Grace-land, in Mem-phis, Ten-nes-see; I'm go-ing to Grace - land.
(Verse 2 see block lyrics)

Poor boys__ and pil-grims with fam-il-ies,__ and we are go-ing to Grace - land.

And my trav-'ling com-pan-ion is nine years__ old,__ he is the child__

wind blow." I'm go-ing to Grace- Ooh, in

Grace-land, Grace-land. I'm go-ing to Grace - land.

For rea - sons I can - not ex - plain, there's some part of me wants to see Grace-

- land. And I may be ob - liged to de- fend ev-'ry love,

ev-'ry end-ing, or may-be there's no ob - li-ga - tions now. May - be I've a

reason to be - lieve we all will be re - ceived in Grace - land.

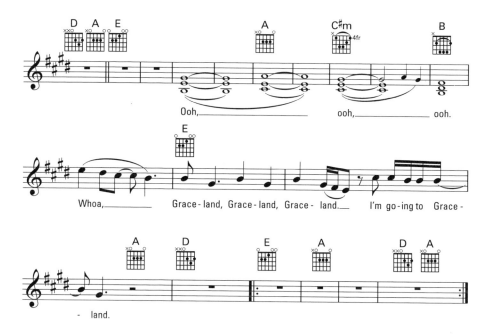

Ooh,_____ ooh,_____ ooh.

Whoa,_____ Grace-land, Grace-land, Grace-land.__ I'm go-ing to Grace-

- land.

Verse 2:
I'm going to Graceland, Graceland
In Memphis, Tennessee
I'm going to Graceland
Poor boys and pilgrims with families
And we are going to Graceland
And my trav'ling companions are ghosts and empty sockets
I'm looking at ghosts and empties
But I've reason to believe
We all will be received in Graceland.

Verse 4:
There is a girl in New York City
Who calls herself the human trampoline
And sometimes when I'm falling
Flying or tumbling in turmoil I say
"Whoa! So, this is what she means."
She means we're bouncing into Graceland
And I see losing love is like a window in your heart
Ev'rybody sees you're blown apart
Ev'rybody feels the wind blow.

Have I Told You Lately

Words & Music by Van Morrison

1, 3, 5. Have I told you late-ly that I love___ you,___

(Verse 2 see block lyrics)
4° Piano solo till *

have I told you there's no - one___ a - bove___ you,___

fill my heart with glad - ness, take a - way my sad - ness,

ease my trou - bles that's what you do. 2. Oh the

do. There's a love that's di - vine___

and it's yours and it's mine,___ like the sun.___

Verse 2:
Oh the morning sun in all its glory
Greets the day with hope and comfort too
And you fill my life with laughter
You can make it better
Ease my troubles that's what you do.

He Ain't Heavy, He's My Brother

Words by Bob Russell • Music by Bobby Scott

1. The road is long_____ with ma-ny a

(Verses 2 & 3 see block lyrics)

wind-ing turn that leads us___ to who___ knows where, who knows

where. But I'm strong,_____ strong e-nough

to car-ry him. He ain't hea-vy, he's my

To Coda ⊕

1.

bro-ther._____ 2. So on we If I'm la-den___ at

2.

all,_____ I'm la-den___ with sad-ness___ that ev-'ry___ one's

Verse 2:
So on we go, his welfare is my concern
No burden is he to bear, we'll get there
For I know he would not encumber me
He ain't heavy, he's my brother.

Verse 3:
It's a long, long road, from which there is no return
While we're on the way to there, why not share
And the load doesn't weigh me down at all
He ain't heavy, he's my brother.

Here Comes The Rain Again

Words & Music by A. Lennox & D.A. Stewart

Verse 2:
Here comes the rain again
Falling on my head like a tragedy
Tearing me apart like a new emotion
I want to breathe in the open wind
I want to kiss like lovers do
Want to dive into your ocean
Is it raining with you?

Verse 3:
Here comes the rain again
Falling on my head like a memory
Falling on my head like a new emotion
I want to walk in the open wind
I want to talk like lovers do
Want to dive into your ocean
Is it raining with you?

Heaven

Words & Music by Bryan Adams & Jim Vallance

1. Oh, think-in' a-bout all our young - er years, there was
(Verse 2 see block lyrics)
on - ly you and me, we were young and wild and free.

Now noth-ing can take you a-way from me, we've been down that road be-fore but that's

o - ver now. You keep me com-ing back for more.

Ba-by you're all that I want, when you're ly-ing here in my arms. I'm

find-ing it hard to be - lieve we're in heav-en. And

love is all___ that I___ need   and I found it there in your___heart.   It

is-n't too hard___ to see___ we're in heav-en.___

heav-en.___   Yeah!___

I've been wait-ing for___ so   long,___   for some-thing___ to ar - rive;___

for love to come a-long.___   Now our dreams are com-ing true,

___ through the good times and the bad.___   Yeah, I'll be stand-ing there by___ you,___ oh!

(Guitar solo)

And

91

Verse 2:
Oh, once in your life you find someone
Who will turn your world around
Bring you up when you're feeling down
Yeah, nothing can change what you mean to me
Oh, there's lots that I could say but just hold me now
'Cause our love will light the way.

Hit The Road Jack

Back in 1961 'Hit The Road Jack' introduced a welcome bit of R&B grit to the Billboard Top 100 No. 1 spot. Preceded there by Bobby Vee's 'Take Good Care Of My Baby' and to be followed by Dion's 'Runaround Sue', this Ray Charles hit was in marked contrast to the prevailing pop mood of the day, bringing a muscular call-and-response treatment to the Percy Mayfield composition and so helping to define Charles' potent brand of soul. The Animals, Suzi Quattro, Buster Poindexter and Basement Jaxx have all revisited the song over the years but it is the Ray Charles version that effortlessly sounds not just like the definitive version, but really the only version.

Hit The Road Jack

Words & Music by Percy Mayfield

(Hit the road,____ Jack and don't you come____ back no

more, no more, no more, no more. Hit the road,____ Jack and don't you come back no

more.)_____ What you___ say?_____ (Hit the Woah,

wo-man, oh wo-man, don't treat me so___ mean; you're the mean-est old wo-man that I've

ev- er seen. I guess if___ you said so,_____ I'll have to pack my things and___

go. (That's right! Hit the road,____ Jack and don't you come_ back no

94

don't you come back no more, no more, no more, no more. Hit the road,___ Jack and

1.

don't you come___ back no more.)_____ What you___ say? (Hit the

2.

Well?___

more.) (Don't you come___ back no more.) (And

(Spoken) Uh, what you say?___

I did - n't un - der-stand you!

don't you come___ back no more.) (Don't you come___ back no

Repeat to fade

more.) (And don't you come back no more.) (Don't you come back no
1. You can't mean that! Oh,___ now ba - by, please!
2. What you tryin' to do to me? Oh, don't treat me like that!

96

Hold On

Words & Music by KT Tunstall & Edwin Makromallis

1. Say you__ to me,__ you're a bird with an eye for an-y-thing shin-y;__
(Verse 2 see block lyrics)

__ search-ing the land for a he-ro__ of a man. You say__ I need

more than my__ fair share of at-ten-tion,__ but I think_you know that__ just is-n't so.

Oh, un-der-neath I felt the fire__ of a burn-ing ques-tion__ tear-ing me__ a-part__

right from the ver-y start. And now I see_ that it don't take a trick of the light to ex-cite me.

__ So__ strong, so__ long, you'll__ see.__ Hold____ on__ to what you've been giv-

98

I felt a change a-com-ing._ I felt a change_ a-com-ing____ soon._ Oh.____

Hold_ on_ to what you've_ been giv-en_ late-ly. Hold_ on_ to what you

know you've got.____ Hold___ on_ to what you've been giv - en_ late-ly. Hold

1. *Repeat ad lib.*

____ on_ 'cause the world will turn_ if you're read-y or_ not._

2.

read-y or_ not._ Oh,_ yeah._ Well, the world will turn_ if you're

read-y or_ not. Oh!_____ Yes, the world will turn_ if you're read-y or_ not._

Verse 2:
Simplicity, a heart of gold
An old head on young shoulders
Quiet and lovely, becoming part of me
And now I see from a handful of names
And a thousand faces
One light burning fiercely.

How Soon Is Now?

Words & Music by Morrissey & Johnny Marr

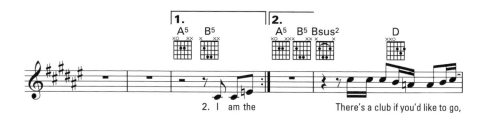

2. I am the   There's a club if you'd like to go,

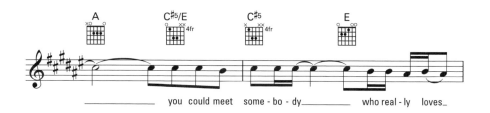

you could meet some - bo - dy_____ who real - ly loves_

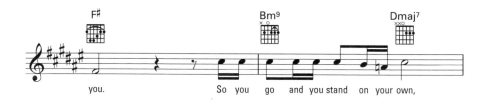

you.   So you   go   and you stand   on   your own,

and you leave on your own,   and you   go home   and you cry and you want to   die._

Repeat to fade

101

Human Nature

Words & Music by Steve Porcaro & John Bettis

1. Look - ing out 'cross the night- time, the ci - ty winks a sleep-less eye. Hear her voice shake my win- dow, sweet se-du - cing sighs. Get me out in - to the night- time,

(Verse 2 see block lyrics)

four walls won't hold me to - night. If this town is just an ap- ple, then let me take a bite. If they say "why, why", tell 'em that it's hu - man na - ture,

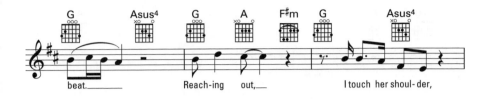

beat.___ Reach-ing out,___ I touch her shoul- der,

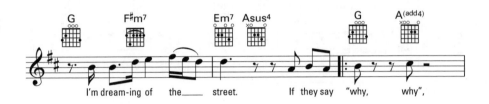

I'm dream-ing of the___ street. If they say "why, why",

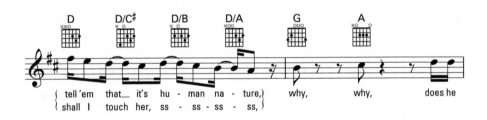

{ tell 'em that___ it's hu - man na - ture,} why, why, does he
{ shall I touch her, ss - ss - ss - ss, }

do me that way? If they say "why, why", ooh,___ sev- en,

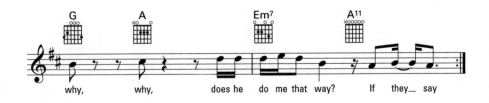

why, why, does he do me that way? If they___ say

104

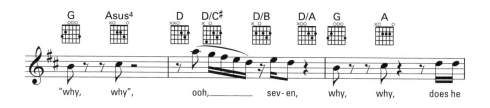

"why, why", ooh,_____ sev-en, why, why, does he

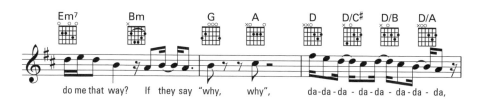

do me that way? If they say "why, why", da-da-da - da-da - da-da - da,

why, why, does he do me that way? I like liv-ing this way, wah -

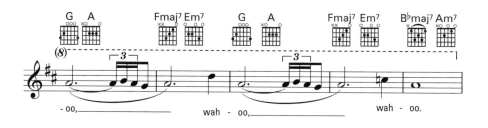

- oo,_____ wah - oo,_____ wah - oo.

Repeat to fade

Verse 2:
Reaching out to touch a stranger
Electric eyes are ev'rywhere
See that girl, she knows I'm watching
She likes the way I stare.

Hot Fun In The Summertime

Words & Music by Sylvester Stewart

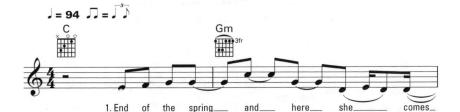

1. End of the spring___ and___ here___ she___ comes___

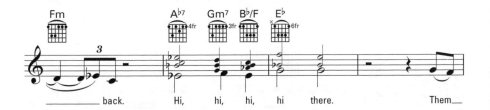

___ back. Hi, hi, hi, hi there. Them___

sum - mer___ days,___ those_ sum - mer___ days.___

___ 2. That's when I had___ most_ of___ my___ fun_

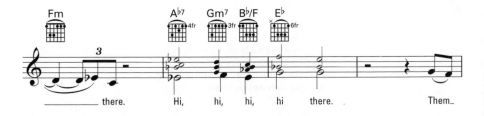

___ there. Hi, hi, hi, hi there. Them_

I Got You (I Feel Good)

James Brown's best-known version of 'I Got You' came out on the King label in late 1965 and soon became one of his signature tunes. In fact it had already been recorded by one of his girl back-up singers in 1962 and on a Smash Records album by Brown himself in 1964. However, due to label disputes, his first recording — with composer credit given to one Ted Wright— was never released as a single and by the time Brown re-recorded it for King, it had mysteriously become one of his own compositions. His much-sampled screams at the beginning and end of the King version became as instantly recognisable as any logo, and over the years the song was to feature in very many movies and TV shows ranging from *White Men Can't Jump* to *The Simpsons*.

I Got You (I Feel Good)

Words & Music by James Brown

Verse 2:
I feel nice, like sugar and spice
I feel nice, like sugar and spice
So nice, so nice, I got you.

111

I Touch Myself

Words & Music by Tom Kelly, Billy Steinberg, Christine Amphlett & Mark McEntee

1. I love my - self__ I want you to love__ me, when I feel down I

(Verse 2 see block lyrics)

want you a - bove__ me, I search my - self__ I want you to find__ me I for-

-get my - self__ I want you__ to re - mind__ me.__ I don't want a -

- ny bo - dy else, when I think a - bout you I touch my - self.__ I

I don't want__ a - ny - bo - dy else oh no oh no

To Coda ⊕

oh no. You're the one who makes me come run - ning,__

112

113

when I think a-bout you I touch my - self. I____ I don't want a -

\- ny bo - dy else, oh no___ oh no___ oh no.__

(Spoken) I want you   I don't want anybody else   and when I think about you,   I touch myself. Ooh

ooh   ooh   ah ah ah ah ah ah ah ah

I don't want   a — ny bo - dy else,   when I think a - bout you__

touch my - self,__ oh oh oh   I don't want   a — ny bo - dy else,

when   I   think   a - bout   you   I   touch   my - self__   I   touch   my -

Repeat to fade

Verse 2:
I close my eyes and see you before me
Think I would die if you were to ignore me
If you could see just how much I adore you
I get down on my knees I'd do anything for you.

114

I'm Outta Love

Words & Music by Anastacia, Sam Watters & Louis Biancaniello

Verse 2:
Said how many times
Have I tried to turn this love around
But every time you just let me down
Come on, be a man about it
You'll survive sure that you can work it out alright
Tell me yesterday, did you know
I'd be the one to let you go?

I'd Like To Teach The World To Sing

Words & Music by Roger Cook, Roger Greenaway, Bill Backer & Billy Davis

I'd like to build the world a home and fur-nish it with love,

grow ap-ple trees and hon-ey bees and

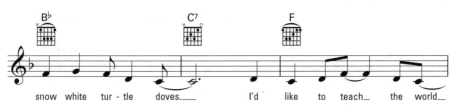

snow white tur-tle doves. I'd like to teach the world

to sing in per-fect har-mo-ny, I'd

like to hold it in my arms and keep it com-pa-ny.

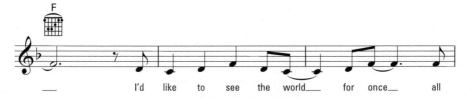

I'd like to see the world for once all

standing hand in hand,____ and hear them ech-o through____ the hills____ for peace through out the land.____ That's the song I hear,____ let the world sing to-day,____ a song of peace that ech-oes on____ and nev-er goes a-way.____ Put your hand in my hand, let's be-gin to-day. Put your hand in my hand, help me find the way. I'd

Fine

D.S. al Fine

119

In Between Days

Words & Music by Robert Smith

1. Yes - ter - day____ I got____ so old____ I
(Verse 2 see block lyrics)

felt like I____ could die,____ yes - ter - day____ I got____

____ so old____ it made me want to cry.____ Go on____

____ go on____ just walk____ a - way__ go on____ go on,____ your choice____

is made.__ Go on__ go on____ and dis - ap - pear,__ go on__

____ go on____ a - way____ from here.____ And I

120

Verse 2:
Yesterday I got so scared I shivered like a child
Yesterday away from you it froze me deep inside
Come back, come back, don't walk away
Come back, come back, come back today
Come back, come back, why can't you see
Come back, come back, come back to me.

It's A Sin

Words & Music by Neil Tennant & Chris Lowe

♩ = 130

Cm · Fm

1. When I look back up - on___ my life,___
(Verses 2 & 3 see block lyrics)

B♭ · E♭ · A♭

___ it's al - ways with a sense_ of shame,_ I've al - ways

Fm · G

been the one_ to_ blame.

Cm · Fm · B♭

For ev - 'ry - thing I___ long_ to do,___ no mat - ter

E♭ · A♭ · Fm

when or where or___ who,___ has one thing in com - mon too:___

G

___ It's a, it's a, it's a,___ it's a sin,

123

Verse 2:
At school they taught me how to be
So pure in thought and word and deed
They didn't quite succeed.

Verse 3:
So I look back upon my life
Forever with a sense of shame
I've always been the one to blame.

125

It Must Be Love

Words & Music by Labi Siffre

Verse 2:
I've got to be near you ev'ry night
Ev'ry day, I couldn't be happy any other way.

127

It's Not Unusual

Words & Music by Gordon Mills & Les Reed

1. It's not un - us - u - al__ to be loved by an - y - one.__
(Verses 2 & 3 see block lyrics)

It's not un - us - u - al__ to have fun with an - y - one.__

But when I see__ you hang - ing a - bout__ with an - y - one,

it's not un - us - u - al__ {to} {it} see me cry.__

I wan-na die.__ hap - pens ev - ery day,__

no mat - ter what_ you say.__ You'll find it

hap-pens___ all the time._____ Love will nev-er do___

C

Dm7 G7

___ what you want_ it to._____ Why can't this

D.C. al Coda

Em E♭9 Dm7 G7

cra-zy love_ be mine?_____

⊕ Coda Cmaj7 Dm7 Em7

find that I'm in love___ with you._ Woh,_ woh,_____

Dm7 Em7 *fade to end* Dm7 Em7 Dm7

___ woh,_ woh,_____ woh,_ woh,_____

Dm7 Em7 Dm7 Cmaj7

___ woh,_ woh, woh, woh,_____ woh,_ woh.___

Verse 2:
It's not unusual to go out at any time
But when I see you go out and about it's such a crime
If you should ever want to be loved by anyone
It's not unusual
It happens every day, *etc.*

Verse 3:
It's not unusual to be mad with anyone
It's not unusual to be sad with anyone
But if I ever find you've changed at any time
It's not unusual to find that I'm in love with you
Woh, woh, *etc.*

129

(I've Had)
The Time
Of My Life

This superhit, as recorded by Bill Medley and Jennifer Warnes, is famous for providing the musical money shot in the movie *Dirty Dancing* (1987). Ex-Leonard Cohen back-up singer Warnes had already enjoyed one major duet hit with Joe Cocker ('Up Where We Belong', page 232) and here she sang just as well with ex-Righteous Brother Medley. Together they provided the soundtrack climax for a movie whose critical reception was notable for its unashamed reinforcement of 80s sexual stereotypes: the ultimate chick flick...*Star Wars* for girls...cheesy but romantic. At the start mousy Jennifer Grey can't dance a lick, but at the end hunky dance instructor Patrick Swayze (in the role that he would never quite shake off) carries her aloft in a triumphant, fear-conquering sequence now usually tagged as 'the most goosebump-inducing dance scene in movie history'.

(I've Had) The Time Of My Life

Words & Music by Frankie Previte, John DeNicola & Donald Markowitz

♩ = 112

(M) 1. I've been wait-ing for so long,___ now I've fi-nal-ly found some-one to stand by

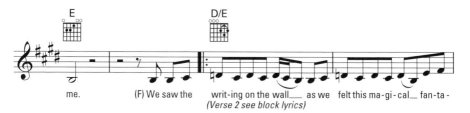

me. (F) We saw the writ-ing on the wall___ as we felt this ma-gi-cal___ fan-ta-
(Verse 2 see block lyrics)

(2° lower harmonies only)

- sy.___ (Both) Now with pas-sion in our eyes___ there's no

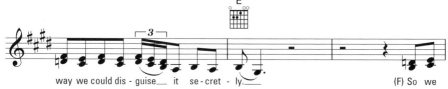

way we could dis-guise___ it se-cret-ly.___ (F) So we

take each oth-er's hand 'cause we seem to un-der-stand the ur-gen-cy.

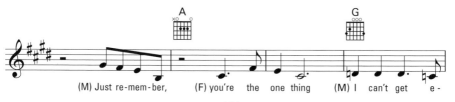

(M) Just re-mem-ber, (F) you're the one thing (M) I can't get e-

131

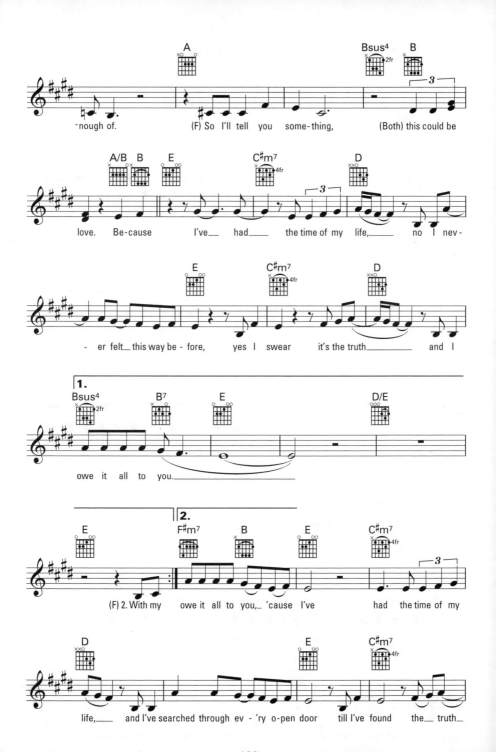

-nough of. (F) So I'll tell you some-thing, (Both) this could be

love. Be-cause I've__ had__ the time of my life,__ no I nev-

- er felt__ this way be - fore, yes I swear it's the truth__ and I

1.

owe it all to you.__

2.

(F) 2. With my owe it all to you,__ 'cause I've had the time of my

life,__ and I've searched through ev - 'ry o-pen door till I've found the__ truth__

Chords above the staff:

| D | B | E | D/E | B | Fsus⁴ |

and I   owe it all to you._____

| E | C#m⁷ |

(Both) I've   had   the   time   of   my
       I've   had   the   time   of   my

| D |

life_____   no I   nev - er felt____ this way be -
life_____   and I've   searched____ through ev - 'ry o - pen

| E | C#m⁷ |

- fore,   yes I   swear   it's   the   truth,__
  door   till   I've   found   the   truth,__

| D | F#m⁷ | F#m⁷/B |

Repeat to fade

_____   and I   owe it all to you.____ 'cause__
_____   and I   owe it all to you.____ 'cause__

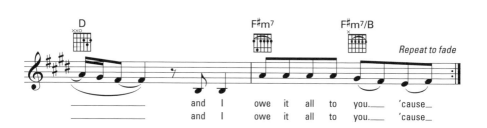

Verse 2:
(F) With my body and soul I want you more than you'll ever know
(M) So we'll just let it go don't be afraid to lose control, no
Yes I know what's on your mind when you say "Stay with me tonight."

133

Jailbreak

Words & Music by Phil Lynott

(Original key A♭ major. To match original recording tune guitar down one semitone)

1. To - night there's gon - na be a   jail__ break,

(Verses 2 & 3 see block lyrics)

some-where in this town.__   See, me and the boys, we don't like it,__

so we're get-tin' up and go-in'   down.__   Hid-in' low, look-in' right to   left.__

If you see us com - in' I think it's__best   to move a-way. Do you hear what I say,   from

un - der my breath?   To - night there's gon - na be a   jail - break,

some-where in__ the town.__   To - night there's gon - na be a

Verse 2:
Tonight there's gonna be trouble
Some of us won't survive
See, the boys and me mean business
Bustin' out dead or alive
I can hear hound dogs on my trail
All hell breaks loose, alarm and sirens wail
Like a game, if you lose go to jail!

Verse 3:
Tonight there's gonna be a breakout
Into the city zones
Don't you dare try to stop us
No one could for long
Search light on my trail
Tonight's the night, all systems fail
Hey you! Good lookin' female come here.

Le Freak

Words & Music by Bernard Edwards & Nile Rodgers

Freak out! Le Freak, c'est chic, freak

out! Freak out! Le

Freak, c'est chic, freak out!

Have you heard a - bout the new dance craze? Lis-ten to us, I'm
(Verse 2 see block lyrics)

sure you'll be a - mazed. Big fun to be had by ev - 'ry - one.

It's up to you, it sure - ly can be done.

Young and old are do-ing it I'm told, just one try and
you too will be sold. It's called Le Freak, they're
do-in' it night and day, Al-low us, we'll
show you the way. Freak out! Le Freak, c'est chic, freak

1, 2.   **3.**

out!   Freak

Verse 2:
All that pressure got you down
Has your head spinning all around
Feel the rhythm, chant the rhyme
Come on along and have a real good time
Like the days of stomping at the Savoy
Now we freak, oh what a joy
Just come on down, to the 54
Find a spot out on the floor.

Just The Two Of Us

Words & Music by Bill Withers, Ralph MacDonald & William Salter

1. I see the cry-stal rain-drops fall, and the beau-ty of it

(Verses 2 & 3 see block lyrics)

all, is when the sun comes shin-ing through. To make those rain-bows in my

mind, when I think of you some-time, and I want to spend some time with you. Just the

two of us, we can make it if we try, just the two of us, just the

two of us. Just the two of us, build-ing cast-les in the sky, just the

1, 2.　　　**3.**　　*molto rall.*

two of us, you and I.

Verse 2:
We look for love, no time for tears
Wasted water all that is
And it don't make no flowers grow
Good things might come to those who wait
Not for those who wait too late
We gotta go for all we know.

Verse 3:
I hear the crystal raindrops fall
On the window down the hall
And it becomes the morning dew
And darlin' when the morning comes
And I see the morning sun
I want to be the one with you.

138

Little Red Corvette

Words & Music by Prince

1. I guess I should have known,_ by the way you parked your car_ side-ways,_
(Verse 2 see block lyrics)

— that it would-n't last. See you're the kind of per-son, who be-

- lieves in mak-ing out once, love'em and leave'em fast.__ I

guess I must be dumb, 'cause you'd a pock-et full of hor-ses,_ Troj-an and some of them used.

But it was Sat-urd-ay night, I guess that makes it all__ right and you say

what have I got to lose? And hon-ey I say:

139

Verse 2:
Guess I should have closed my eyes
When you drove me to the place where your horses run free
'Cause I felt a little ill when I saw
All the pictures of the jockeys that had been there before me
Believe it or not I started to worry
I wondered if I had enough class
But it was Saturday night, I guess that makes it all right and you say:
"Baby, have you got enough gas?"

Life On Mars?

Words & Music by David Bowie

♩ = 60 (a tempo on repeat)

It's a God-aw-ful small af-fair *(Verse 2 see block lyrics)* to the girl with the mou - sy hair,

but her mum-my is yell - ing "No", and her dad-dy has told_ her to go.

But her friend is no-where to be seen, now she walks through her sunk-en dream

to the seat with the clear-est view, and she's hooked to the sil - ver screen.

But the film is a sad-dening bore, for she's lived it ten times or more.

poco rall.

She could spit in the eyes_ of fools as they ask her to fo - cus on

Verse 2:
It's on Amerika's tortured brow that Mickey Mouse has grown up a cow
Now the workers have struck for fame 'cause Lennon's on sale again
See the mice in their million hordes from Ibiza to the Norfolk Broads
Rule Britannia is out of bounds to my mother, my dog and clowns
But the film is a saddening bore 'cause I wrote it ten times or more
It's about to be writ again as I ask her to focus on...

Like A Virgin

Words & Music by Billy Steinberg & Tom Kelly

1. I made it through the wil - der - ness.___ Some - how I made it through.___

(Verse 2 see block lyrics)

Did - n't know how lost___ I was___ un - til I___ found you.___

I was beat,___ in - com - plete.___ I'd been had.___ I was sad_

(Verse 3 see block lyrics)

___ and blue. But you made me feel,___ yeah, you made___ me feel_

___ shin - y and new.___ Like a

vir - gin, (hey) touched for the ver - y first time. Like a

Verse 2:
Gonna give you all my love, boy
My fear is fading fast
Been saving it all for you
'Cause only love can last
You're so fine, and you're mine
Make me strong, yeah, you make me bold
Oh, your love thawed out, yeah your love thawed out
What was scared and cold.

Verse 3:
You're so fine and you're mine
I'll be yours till the end of time
'Cause you made me feel
Yeah, you made me feel
I've nothing to hide.

147

Love Is In The Air

Words & Music by Harry Vanda & John Young

1. Love is in the air, ev - 'ry - where I look a -
(Verses 2-4. see block lyrics)
- round.

Love is in the air, ev - 'ry sight and ev' - ry
sound. And I don't know if

I'm be - ing fool - ish, don't know if I'm be - ing wise.

— But it's some - thing that I must be - lieve in, and it's

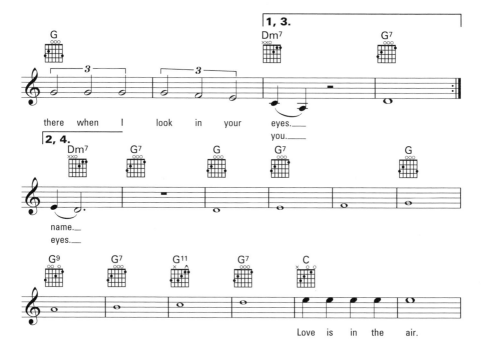

there when I look in your eyes.___

you.___

name.___

eyes.___

Love is in the air.

Love is in the air, oh, oh.

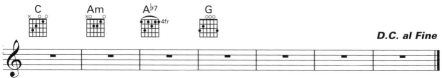

D.C. al Fine

Verse 2:
Love is in the air, in the whisper of the trees
Love is in the air, in the thunder of the sea
And I don't know if I'm just dreaming
Don't know if I feel sane
But it's something that I must believe in
And it's there when you call out my name.

Verse 3:
Love is in the air, in the rising of the sun
Love is in the air, when the day is nearly done
And I don't know if you're an illusion
Don't know if I see it true
But you're something that I must believe in
And you're there when I reach out for you.

Verse 4:
Love is in the air, ev'rywhere I look around
Love is in the air, ev'ry sight and ev'ry sound
And I don't know if I'm being foolish
Don't know if I'm being wise
But it's something that I must believe in
And it's there when I look in your eyes.

149

Love Will Tear Us Apart

Ian Curtis' song became an instant legend when, in May 1980 (the month following its release) his suicide threw it into a harsh and unexpected spotlight. Curtis had written it in 1979 and the song was introduced into the band's repertoire when Joy Division supported Buzzcocks on a UK tour towards the end of that year. At about the same time it was recorded for a John Peel session. In retrospect the song's troubled lyrics took on a dark resonance and it came as no surprise that Curtis' widow Deborah had its title inscribed on his memorial stone. The lyric had originally seemed to discuss their fraught relationship, but now it was hard not to see it as a fatal prediction. Not for the first time a posthumous hit assumed premonitory overtones, as had happened with Buddy Holly's *It Doesn't Matter Anymore*.

Joy Division

Love Will Tear Us Apart

Words & Music by Ian Curtis, Peter Hook, Bernard Sumner & Stephen Morris

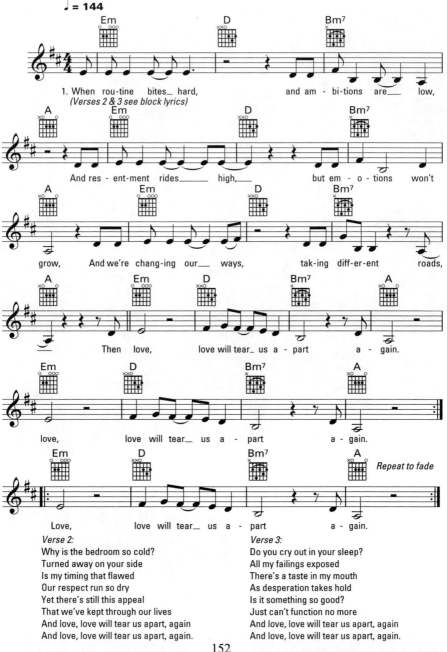

♩ = 144

1. When rou-tine bites_ hard, and am - bi-tions are_ low,
(Verses 2 & 3 see block lyrics)

And res - ent-ment rides_____ high,___ but em - o - tions won't

grow, And we're chang-ing our_ ways, tak-ing diff-er-ent roads,

Then love, love will tear_ us a - part a - gain.

love, love will tear_ us a - part a - gain.

Repeat to fade

Love, love will tear_ us a - part a - gain.

Verse 2:
Why is the bedroom so cold?
Turned away on your side
Is my timing that flawed
Our respect run so dry
Yet there's still this appeal
That we've kept through our lives
And love, love will tear us apart, again
And love, love will tear us apart, again.

Verse 3:
Do you cry out in your sleep?
All my failings exposed
There's a taste in my mouth
As desperation takes hold
Is it something so good?
Just can't function no more
And love, love will tear us apart, again
And love, love will tear us apart, again.

152

Massachusetts

Words & Music by Barry Gibb, Maurice Gibb & Robin Gibb

Verse 2:
Tried to hitch a ride to San Francisco
Gotta do the things I wanna do
And the lights all went out in Massachusetts
They brought me back to see my way with you.

Verse 3:
Talk about the life in Massachusetts
Speak about the people I have seen
And the lights all went out in Massachusetts
And Massachusetts is one place I have seen.

The Model

Words & Music by Ralf Hutter, Karl Bartos & Emil Schult

Verse 2:
She's going out tonight, but drinking just champagne
And she has been checking nearly all the men
She's playing her game, and you can hear them say
"She is looking good, for beauty we will pay."

Verse 3:
She's posing for consumer products now and then
For ev'ry camera she gives the best she can
I saw her on the cover of a magazine
Now she's a big success I want to meet her again.

Move Over Darling

Words & Music by Joe Lubin, Hal Kanter & Terry Melcher

way you sigh has me wav-ing my con-science bye-
- bye. You can call me a fick-le thing, but I'm prac-tic-'lly yours for-
- ev-er be-cause... I yearn to be kissed. Move ov-er darl-ing.
(How can I re-sist?)
Move ov-er darl-ing. You've cap-tured my heart and now that I'm no long-er
free. Make love to me.
(The way you sigh has me
wav-ing my con-science good-bye.) You can call me a fick-le

157

thing,   but I'm   prac-tic-'lly yours   for - ev - er   be - cause... I

yearn to   be kissed.   Move ov - er   darl - ing. How   can   I   re - sist?

Move ov - er   darl - ing. Please give me your love,   I'm   long-ing for   you._____ I

need   all your love,   ho - nest   I   do._____ You've cap-tured my heart   and

now that   I'm   no   long - er   free,_____   make   love   to

Repeat ad lib. to fade

me.   Make love to   me._____   Make love   to

158

Mr. Brightside

Words & Music by Brandon Flowers, Dave Keuning, Mark Stoermer & Ronnie Vannucci

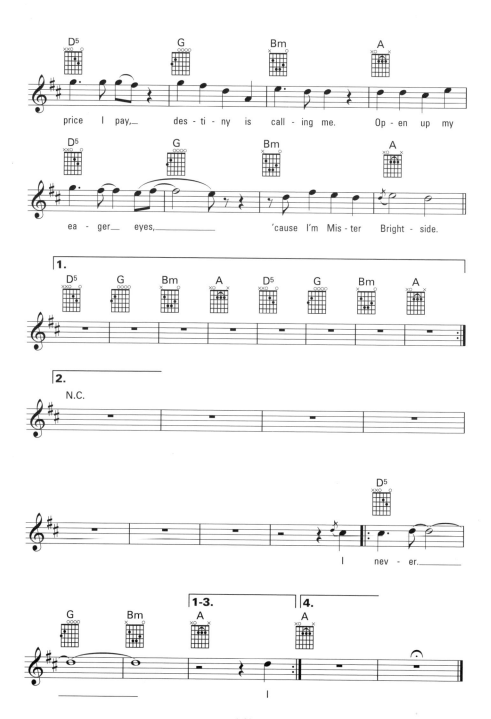

price I pay,_ des - ti - ny is call - ing me. Op - en up my

ea - ger_ eyes,_____ 'cause I'm Mis - ter Bright - side.

1.

2.

N.C.

I nev - er.____

1-3. **4.**

I

Once In A Lifetime

Words & Music by David Byrne, Brian Eno, Jerry Harrison, Tina Weymouth & Christopher Frantz

♩ = 118

And you may find your-self liv-ing in a shot-gun shack.

And you may find your-self in an-oth-er part of the world.

And you may find your-self be-hind the wheel of a

large au-to-mo-bile. And you may find your-self in a beau-ti-ful

house, with a beau-ti-ful wife. And

you may ask___ your-self "Well, how did I get

162

here?" Let - ting the days go by,__ let the wa-ter hold me down, let-ting the

days go by,__ wa-ter flow-ing un-der-ground, in - to the blue a - gain,__ af-ter the

mo-ney's gone, once in a life - time,__ wa - ter's flow-ing un - der-

- ground. 2. And you may ask your - self "How do I work this?"

And you may ask your - self "Where is that large au - to-mo-bile?"

And you may tell your - self "This is not my beau-ti-ful

house!" And you may tell your - self "This is not my beau-ti-ful

One More Night

Words & Music by Phil Collins

One more night.___

One more night.___

1. I've been try - ing oh___ so long___ to let you___ know,___
(Verses 2 & 3 see block lyrics)

let you know_ how_ I feel.___

And if I stum - ble or if I fall___ just help me___ back___

so I can make you see.___ Please give me

166

Verse 2:
I've been sitting here so long
Wasting time, just staring at the phone
And I was wond'ring should I call you
Then I thought maybe you're not alone.

Verse 3:
I know there'll never be a time
You'll ever feel the same and I know it's only words
But if you change your mind you know that I'll be here
And maybe we both can learn.

Only The Lonely

Words & Music by Roy Orbison & Joe Melson

1. On - ly the lone - ly know the way I feel to - night,
(Verse 2 see block lyrics)
on - ly the lone - ly know this feel - ing ain't right.
There goes my ba - by, there goes my heart, they've gone for-
-ev - er so far a - part. But on - ly the lone - ly
know why I cry, on - ly the
lone - ly. 2. On - ly the lone - ly.

Verse 2:
Only the lonely know the heartaches I've been through
Only the lonely know I cry and cry for you
Maybe tomorrow, a new romance
No more sorrow, but that's the chance
You've got to take if you're lonely
Heartbreak, only the lonely.

169

Prince Charming

Words & Music by Adam Ant & Marco Pirroni

♩ = 148

Don't you ev - er, don't you ev - er, stop be-ing dan - dy,

show - ing me you're hand - some. Prince Charm - ing! Prince Charm - ing! Rid - i - cule is

noth - ing to be scared of. Don't you ev - er, don't you ev - er, stop be-ing dan - dy,

show - ing me you're hand - some. Don't you ev - er, don't you ev - er,

low - er your self, for - gett-ing all your stand - ards. Prince Charm - ing! Prince Charm - ing!

Rid - i - cule is noth-ing to be scared of. Don't you ev - er, don't you ev - er,

170

stop be-ing dan-dy, show-ing me you're hand-some. Silk or leath-er,

or a feath-er, res-pect your-self and all of those a-round you.

Prince Charm-ing! Prince Charm-ing! Rid-i-cule is noth-ing to be scared of.

Don't you ev-er, don't you ev-er, stop be-ing dan-dy,

show-ing me you're hand-some. Don't you ev-er, don't you ev-er,

low-er your-self, for-gett-ing all your stand-ards. Prince Charm-ing!

Repeat 8 times

Prince Charm-ing! Rid-i-cule is noth-ing to be scared of.

171

Put Your Records On

Words & Music by John Beck, Steven Chrisanthou & Corinne Bailey Rae

1. Three lit-tle birds sat on my win-dow, and they told me I don't need to wor-
(Verse 2 see block lyrics)
-ry. Sum-mer came like cin-na-mon, so___sweet. Lit-tle girls dou-ble dutch on the con-
-crete. May-be some - times___ we___ got it wrong but it's
all right. And no - thing seemed to change.___ the more___ they stay the same.
Don't you he - si-tate. Girl, put your re-cords on,___ tell me your fav-'rite song.
You go a-head, let your hair___ down.___ Sap-phire and fad-ed jeans,

172

I hope you get your dreams. Just go a-head; let your hair___ down.___

You're gon-na find your-self some-where, some - how.___   - where,   some - how.___

___'Twas more than I could take,   pi - ty   for pi-ty's sake.   Some nights kept me a-wake.

I thought that   I   was strong-er.___   When you gon-na re-al-ise___

that you don't ev-en have to   try___ an-y long-er?   Do___ what you want to.___

- where,   some   -   how.

Verse 2:
Blue as the sky, sunburnt and lonely
Sipping tea in a bar by the roadside
Don't you let those other boys fool you
Gotta love that afro hairdo.

Maybe sometimes we feel afraid
But it's all right. The more you stay the same
The more they seem to change
Don't you think it's strange?

173

Rasputin

Words & Music by Frank Farian, George Reyam & Fred Jay

There lived a cer-tain man in Rus-sia long a-go. He was big and strong in his eyes a flam-ing glow. Most peo-ple looked at him with ter-ror and fear but to Mos-cow chicks he was such a love-ly dear. He could preach the Bi-ble like a preach-er, full of ec-sta-sy and fire. But he al-so was the kind of teach-er wo-men would de-sire.

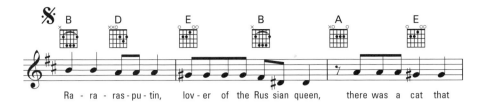

Ra - ra - ras - pu - tin, lov - er of the Rus sian queen, there was a cat that

real - ly was gone._ Ra - ra - ras - pu - tin. Rus - sia's great-est love ma - chine.

1-3. *(last time)* **D.S.** **4.**

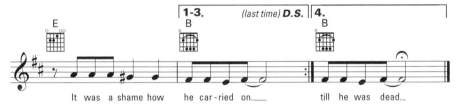

It was a shame how he car - ried on.___ till he was dead._

Verse 2:
He ruled the Russian land and never mind the tsar
But the kasachok he danced really wunderbar
In all affairs of state he was the man to please
But he was real great when he had a girl to squeeze
For the queen he was no wheeler dealer
Though she'd heard the things he'd done
She believed he was a holy healer
Who would heal her son.

Ra ra Rasputin
Lover of the Russian queen
There was a cat that really was gone
Ra ra Rasputin
Russia's greatest love machine
It was a shame how he carried on

(Spoken:)
But when his drinking and lusting and his hunger
for power became known to more and more people
the demands to do something about this outrageous
man became louder and louder.

Verse 3:
"This man's just got to go!" declared his enemies
But the ladies begged "Don't you try to do it, please."
No doubt this Rasputin had lots of hidden charms
Though he was a brute they just fell into his arms
Then one night some men of higher standing
Set a trap, they're not to blame
"Come to visit us." they kept demanding
And he really came.

Ra ra Rasputin
Lover of the Russian queen
They put some poison into his wine
Ra ra Rasputin
Russia's greatest love machine
He drank it all and said "I feel fine."

Ra ra Rasputin
Lover of the Russian queen
They didn't quit, they wanted his head
Ra ra Rasputin
Russia's greatest love machine
And so they shot him till he was dead.
(Spoken:) Oh, those Russians...

175

Real Wild Child (Wild One)

Words & Music by Johnny O'Keefe, Johnny Greenan & Dave Owens

♩ = 146

1. Well I'm - a just out - a-school, like I'm re - al re - al cool, got - ta

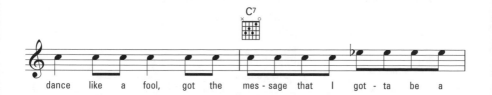

dance like a fool, got the mes - sage that I got - ta be a

wild one, ooh, yeah I'm a wild one___

Gon - na break it loose, I'm gon - na keep 'em mov - in' wild, I'm gon - na

keep a swing - in' ba - by I'm a real wild child.___ 2. Gon - na

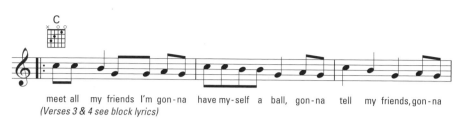

meet all my friends I'm gon-na have my-self a ball, gon-na tell my friends, gon-na
(Verses 3 & 4 see block lyrics)

tell them all that I'm a wild one. Ooh yeah I'm a

wild one._____ Gon-na break it loose, I'm gon-na

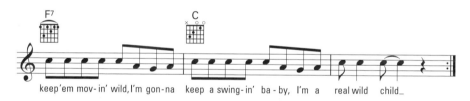

keep 'em mov-in' wild, I'm gon-na keep a swing-in' ba-by, I'm a real wild child_

Verse 3:
I'm a real wild one
And I like a-wild fun
In a world gone crazy
Everything seems hazy
I'm a wild one
Ooh yeah, I'm a wild one.

Verse 4:
I'm a wild one
I'm a wild one
I'm a wild one
Oh baby I'm a wild one.

Rave On

Words & Music by Sunny West, Bill Tilghman & Norman Petty

♩ = 160

N.C.   G5

1. A - w - e - e - e - ell the lit - tle things you___ say and do___
(Verse 2 see block lyrics)

C5

make me want to___ be with you - ou - ou. Rave on it's a cra - zy feel - ing and-a

G5   D5

I know it's got-ta me reel - in' when you say.___ "I love you."_____

1. G5   D5   **2.** G5   C5

Rave on.   2. The   Oh well, rave on,___ it's a

G5

cra - zy feel - in' and-a I know it's got-ten me reel - in', I'm so glad___ that

G5   D5   G5   C5

you're re - veal - in' your_____ love___ for me. Rave on,

178

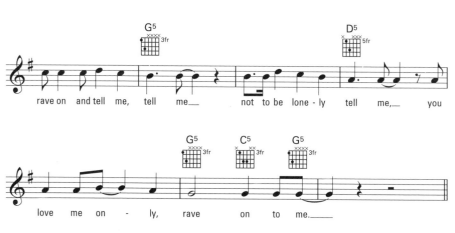

rave on and tell me, tell me— not to be lone - ly tell me,— you

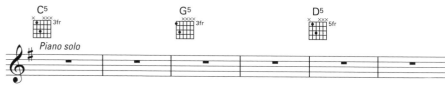

love me on - ly, rave on to me.—

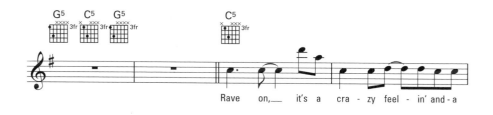

Piano solo

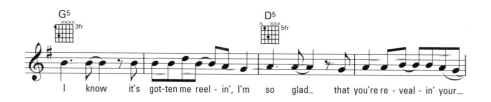

Rave on,— it's a cra - zy feel - in' and - a

I know it's got-ten me reel - in', I'm so glad— that you're re - veal - in' your—

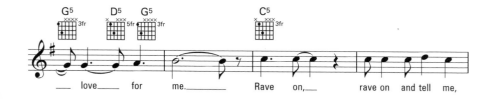

— love— for me.— Rave on,— rave on and tell me,

179

Verse 2:
The way you dance and hold me tight
The way you kiss and say goodnight
Rave on it's a crazy feeling and-a
I know it's gotta me reelin'
When you say "I love you," rave on.

Respect

A song most commonly associated with Aretha Franklin, 'Respect' was in fact written and originally recorded by Otis Redding in 1965. Franklin's version came out two years later and reversed the male's plea for respect from his woman in a famously feisty turn-around that saw The Queen Of Soul at the height of her powers and accompanied by sisters Carolyn and Erma. Perhaps because Franklin's cover was such an international success, Redding's only recorded observation about her version was good-naturedly to call it "the song that little girl done stole from me". The assertive lyric spells out the word R-E-S-P-E-C-T at one point, perhaps inspiring the following year's country hit D-I-V-O-R-C-E, an altogether more sentimental offering.

Respect

Words & Music by Otis Redding

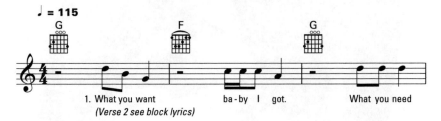

1. What you want   ba-by I got.   What you need
(Verse 2 see block lyrics)

you know I got it.   All I'm ask-in'   is for a lit-tle re-

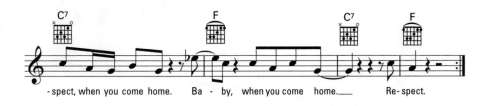

-spect, when you come home.   Ba - by, when you come home.___   Re-spect.

3. I'm out___ to give you   all my mon-ey,   but all I'm ask-in'
(Verse 4 see block lyrics)

is re-turn, ho-ney,   is to give me   my pro-per re-spect when you get

182

home.　　Yeah,　ba - by,　when you get　home.

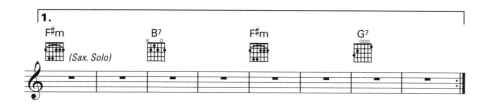

1.

(Sax. Solo)

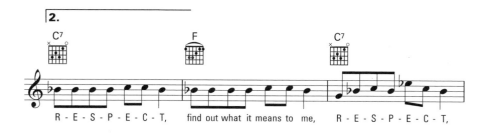

2.

R - E - S - P - E - C - T,　find out what it means to　me,　R - E - S - P - E - C - T,

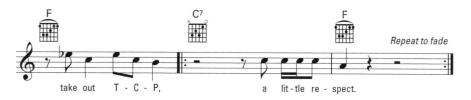

Repeat to fade

take out　T - C - P,　　a　lit - tle re - spect.

Verse 2:
I ain't gonna do you wrong
While you gone
I ain't gonna do you wrong
'Cause I don't wanna.

Verse 4:
Ooh your kisses, sweeter than honey
But guess what so is my money
All I want you to do for me
Is give it to me when you get home
Yeah, baby, when you get home.

Rock Your Baby

Words & Music by Harry Casey & Richard Finch

2°:
Yeah, hold me tight with all your might
Now let your lovin' flow real sweet and slow.

Roll With It

Words & Music by Noel Gallagher

♩ = 130

G7   N.C.

You got-ta   roll   with it,___   you got-ta   take   your time,___   you got-ta

C9   G/B

say what you say, don't let   an-y-bo-dy get in your way,___ 'cause it's all___ too   much___

A7   G

___   for   me   to   take._____   Don't ev - er

G7

stand   a - side,___   don't ev - er   be   de - nied,___   if you wan - na
*Instrumental on D.S. until ***

C   G/B

be who you'd be   if you're com-in' with me.___   I think I've got a feel-in' I've lost___

A7sus4   C   G/B

___ in - side,___   I think I'm gon - na take me   a - way___

185

and hide._ I'm think-ing of things that I_____ just can't_ a - bide._

I know the roads down_ which_

_ your life_____ will drive._ I

find the key that_ lets_ you slip_ in - side._

Kiss the girl,_ she's not_____ be - hind_ the door._

You know I think I re - cog - nise_____ your face_ but I've

nev - er seen you be - fore._ You got - ta

roll with it,___ you got-ta take your time,_ you got-ta say what you say, don't let

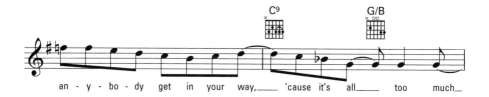

an - y - bo - dy get in your way,___ 'cause it's all___ too much___

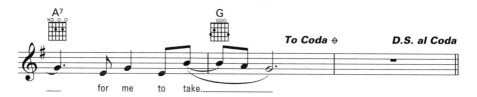

To Coda ⊕   D.S. al Coda

___ for me to take.___

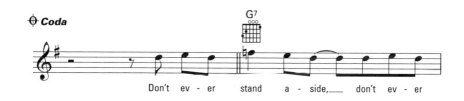

⊕ **Coda**

Don't ev - er stand a - side,___ don't ev - er

be de - nied,_ if you wan-na be who you'd be if you're com-in' with me.___ I

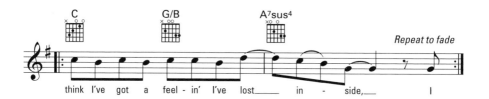

Repeat to fade

think I've got a feel - in' I've lost___ in - side,___ I

187

S.O.S.

Words & Music by Benny Andersson, Stig Anderson & Björn Ulvaeus

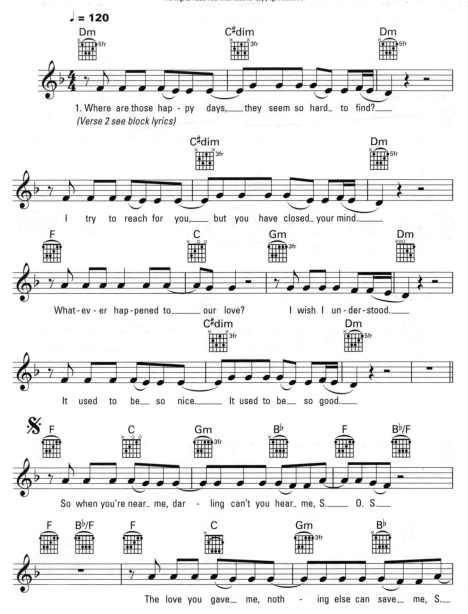

1. Where are those hap - py days,___ they seem so hard_ to find?___
(Verse 2 see block lyrics)

I try to reach for you,___ but you have closed_ your mind.___

What - ev - er hap - pened to___ our love? I wish I un - der - stood.___

It used to be_ so nice.___ It used to be_ so good.___

So when you're near_ me, dar - ling can't you hear_ me, S.___ O. S.___

The love you gave_ me, noth - ing else can save_ me, S.___

Verse 2:
You seem so far away, though you are standing near
You make me feel alive, but something died I fear
I really tried to make it out, I wish I understood
What happed to our love, it used to be so good.

Sailing

Words & Music by Gavin Sutherland

1. I am sail-ing, I am sail-ing home a-gain_ 'cross the
(Verse 2 see block lyrics)
sea. I am sail-ing storm-y wa-ters to be near you, to be free. I am
fly-ing, I am fly-ing like a bird_ 'cross the sky. I am fly-ing, pass-ing

1. high-clouds to be with_ you, to be free. **2.** Can you near you, to be

free.__ Oh, Lord to be near you, to be free;__ oh, Lord to be near you, to be

D.S. *to fade*

free.__ Oh, Lord to be near_ you, to be free, oh, Lord.

Verse 2:
Can you hear me, can you hear me
Through the dark night far away?
I am dying, forever crying
To be with you, who can say

We are sailing, we are sailing
Home again 'cross the sea
We are sailing salty waters
To be near you, to be free.

She's The One

Words & Music by Karl Wallinger

♩ = 78

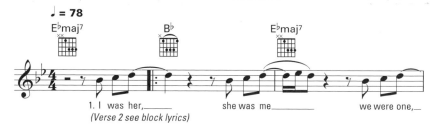

1. I was her,⎯ she was me⎯ we were one,⎯
(Verse 2 see block lyrics)

⎯ we were free.⎯ And if there's some bo - dy call-ing me on,⎯

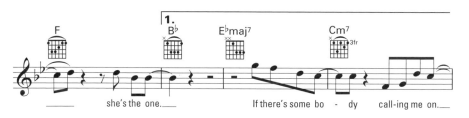

⎯ she's the one.⎯ If there's some bo - dy call-ing me on.⎯

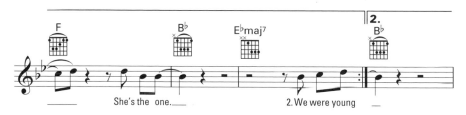

⎯ She's the one.⎯ 2. We were young ⎯

3. When you get to where you wan-na go,⎯ and you

191

know the things you wan-na know,__ you're smil -

- ing.__ When you said what you wan-na say__ and you

know the way you wan-na play,__ it. You'll be so high you'll be fly -

2° say,__

- ing. 4. Though the sea__ will be strong,_____ I know we'll

(Verse 5 see block lyrics)

__ car-ry on._____ 'Cause if there's some-bo - dy call-ing me on__

she's the one._____ If there's some-bo -

- dy call-ing me on_____ she's the one.__

192

Verse 2:
We were young, we were wrong
We were fun, all along
And if there's somebody calling me on
She's the one.

Verse 5:
I was her, she was me
We were one, we were free
And if there's somebody calling me on
She's the one
And if there's somebody calling me on
She's the one.

She's Not There

Words & Music by Rod Argent

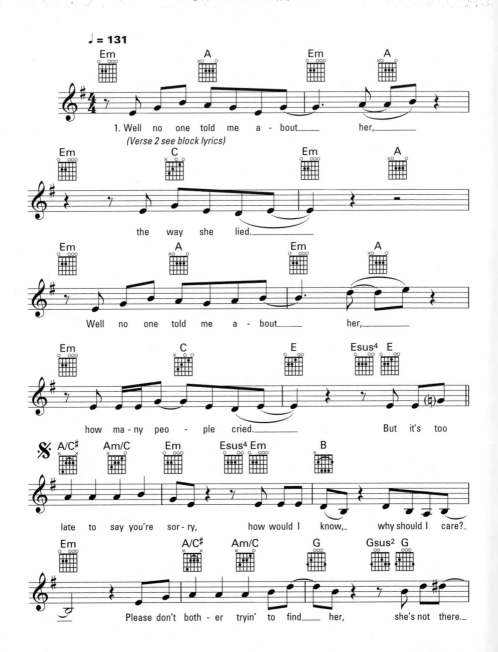

1. Well no one told me a - bout her,

(Verse 2 see block lyrics)

the way she lied.

Well no one told me a - bout her,

how ma - ny peo - ple cried. But it's too

late to say you're sor - ry, how would I know, why should I care?

Please don't both - er tryin' to find her, she's not there.

Verse 2:
Well no one told me about her, what could I do?
Well no one told me about her, though they all knew
But it's too late to say you're sorry, how would I know, why should I care?
Please don't bother tryin' to find her, she's not there
Well let me tell you 'bout the way she looked, the way she acted, the colour of her hair
Her voice was soft and cool, her eyes were clear and bright, but she's not there.

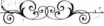

Somewhere Only We Know

Words & Music by Tim Rice-Oxley, Tom Chaplin & Richard Hughes

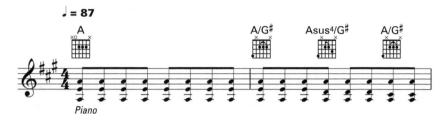

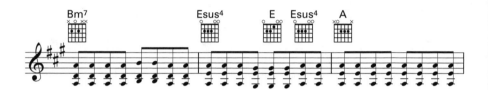

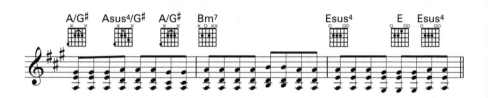

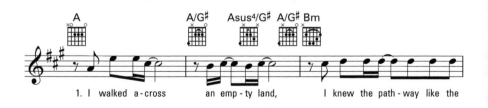

1. I walked a-cross an emp-ty land, I knew the path-way like the

back of my hand.___ I felt the earth be-neath my___ feet,

some - thing to re - ly on. So tell me when you're gon - na let me in,___

I'm get - ting tired and I need some - where to be - gin.___

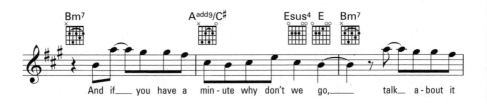

And if___ you have a min - ute why don't we go,___ talk___ a - bout it

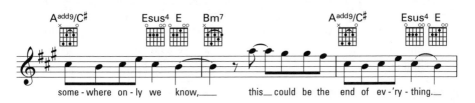

some - where on - ly we know,___ this___ could be the end of ev - 'ry - thing.___

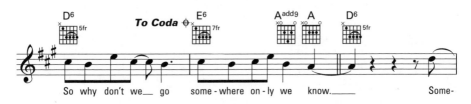

To Coda

So why don't we___ go some - where on - ly we know.___ Some-

D.S. al Coda

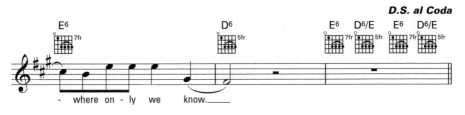

- where on - ly we know.___

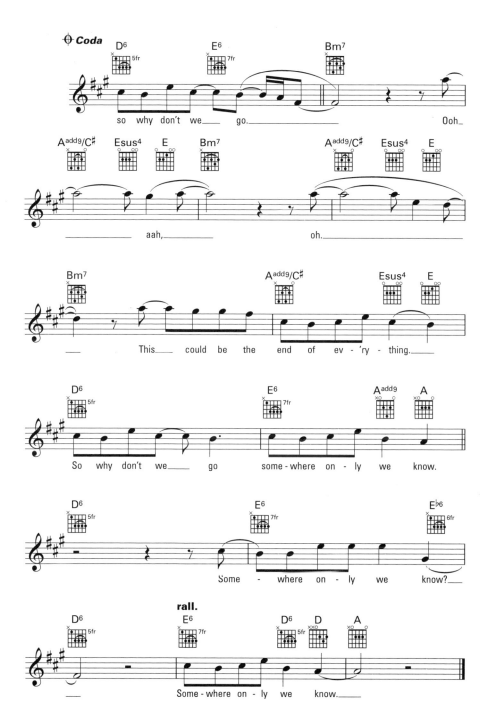

Son Of A Preacher Man

Words & Music by John Hurley & Ronnie Wilkins

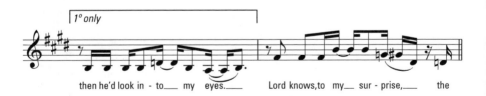

on - ly boy___ who could ev - er teach___ me.___

was the son of a preach-er man. Yes he was,___ he was,___

1. **2.**

Ooh,___ yes he was.
Lord knows, he was.

How well I___ re - mem - ber the look that was in___ his eyes,___

steal-ing kiss-es from me___ on the sly.___ Tak-ing time to make time,___

tell-ing me that he's all___ mine. learn-ing from each oth - er's know-ing,

look - ing to see___ how much___ we've grown.___ And the

201

on - ly one___ who could ev - er reach___ me,

was the son of a preach-er man. The on - ly boy_ who could ev - er teach me,_

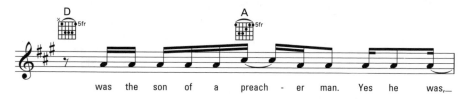

was the son of a preach - er man. Yes he was,_

_ he was,___ oh yes he was._____ (The

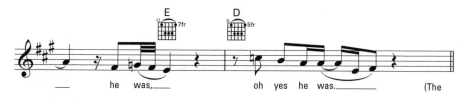

He was a sweet-talk-ing son of a preach-er man._
on - ly one_who could ev - er reach me,   was the son of a preach-er man.   The

Repeat ad lib. to fade

Aw, I guessed he was son of a preach-er man.
on - ly boy_who could ev - er teach me,   was the son of a preach-er man.)

Verse 2:
Being good isn't always easy
No matter how hard I try
When he started sweet-talking to me
He'd come and tell me ev'rything is alright
He'd kiss and tell me ev'rything is alright
Can I get away again tonight?

Sweet Caroline

Words & Music by Neil Diamond

reach - in' out,_____ touch - in' me_____ touch - in'

you._____ Sweet Car - o - line,____

good times nev - er seemed so good._____

I've been in - clined____ to be - lieve____ they nev-er

To Coda

would. But now I... look at the night,_

____ and it don't seem so lone - ly.

We fill it up with on - ly two.

205

Stand by Me

Ben E. King was a doo-wop vocalist in a high school band who subsequently became lead singer with The Five Crowns, a group that soon rechristened itself The Drifters. After their big Doc Pomus/Mort Shuman hit 'Save The Last Dance for Me' King left, went solo and in 1961 had his own top ten hit with Jerry Leiber and Phil Spector's 'Spanish Harlem'. His even bigger follow-up was 'Stand By Me', a song he co-wrote with Jerry Leiber and Mike Stoller. Despite its rather haphazard beginnings (it was put together as something of an afterthought on the 'Spanish Harlem' session) 'Stand By Me' would become a classic, being covered by Otis Redding in 1963 and finding a new audience via John Lennon's 1975 solo *Rock 'n' Roll* album. In 1986 it was featured in, and gave its title to, Rob Reiner's coming-of-age movie based on a Stephen King story. 'Stand By Me' was also co-opted for the latter-day Leiber & Stoller jukebox stage musical *Smokey Joe's Cafe*.

Stand By Me

Words & Music by Ben E. King, Jerry Leiber & Mike Stoller

Verse 2:
If the sky that we look upon should tumble and fall
Or the mountains should crumble to the sea
I won't cry, I won't cry, no, I won't shed a tear
Just as long as you stand, stand by me
Whenever you're in trouble won't you
Stand by me, oh now, now, stand by me
Stand by me, stand by me.

Summer In The City

Words & Music by John Sebastian, Mark Sebastian & Steve Boone

1. Hot town, sum-mer in the ci-ty, back of my neck get-ting dir-ty and grit-ty.

(Verses 2 & 3 see block lyrics)

Been down, is-n't it a pi-ty, does-n't seem to be a sha-dow in the ci-ty.

All a-round peo-ple look-ing half dead, walk-ing on the side-walk, hot-ter than a match head.

But at night it's a diff-'rent world, go out and find a girl.

Come on, come on and dance all night, des-pite the heat it-'ll be all-right. And

babe, don't you know it's a pi-ty the days can't be like the nights in the

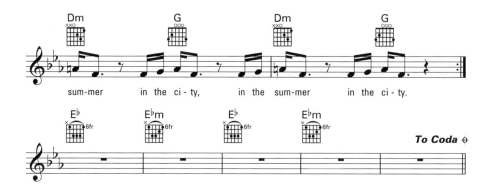

sum-mer   in the ci - ty,   in the sum-mer   in the ci - ty.

To Coda ⊕

D.C. al Coda

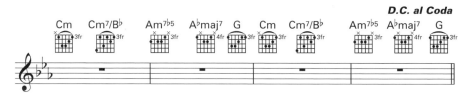

⊕ **Coda**

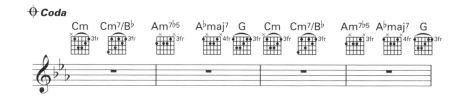

D.S.S. al Coda

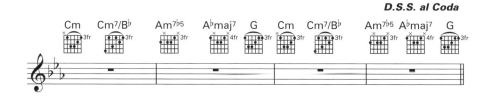

Verse 2:
Cool town, evening in the city
Dressing so fine and looking pretty
Cool cat, looking for a kitty
Gonna look in every corner of the city
Till I'm wheezing like a bus stop
Running up the stairs, gonna meet you on the rooftop.

Verse 3:
Hot town, summer in the city
Back of my neck getting dirty and gritty
Been down, isn't it a pity
Doesn't seem to be a shadow in the city
All around people looking half dead
Walking on the sidewalk, hotter than a match head.

209

There She Goes

Words & Music by Lee Mavers

1. There she goes,___ there she goes___ a - gain,___

(Verses 2 & 3 see block lyrics)

rac - ing through my___ brain.___ And I___ just___ can't con - tain___ this

feel - in'___ that re - mains.___

210

Verse 2:
There she blows, there she blows again
Pulsing through my vein
And I just can't contain this feelin' that remains.

Verse 3:
There she goes, there she goes
Chasing down my lane
And I just can't contain this feelin' that remains.

211

This Love

Words & Music by Adam Levine, James Valentine,
Jesse Carmichael, Mickey Madden & Ryan Dusick

♩ = 92

1. I was so high I did not re-cog-nise the fire burn-ing
(Verse 2 see block lyrics)

in her eyes. The cha-os that con-trolled my mind. Oh! Whis-pered good-bye as she got on

a plane, nev-er to re-turn a-gain but al-ways in my heart. Oh!

This love has ta-ken its toll on me. She said good-bye too ma-ny times be-fore.

And her heart is break-ing in front of me and I have no choice 'cause

I won't say good-bye an-y-more. Whoa, whoa,

Verse 2:
I tried my best to feed her appetite
Keep her coming ev'ry night
So hard to keep her satisfied
Oh! Kept playing love like it was just a game
Pretending to feel the same
Then turn around and leave again.

Time After Time

Words & Music by Cyndi Lauper & Robert Hyman

1. Ly - ing in__ my bed I hear_ the clock tick__ and think of you.__

(Verse 2 see block lyrics)

Caught up__ in cir - cles, con - fu - sion is no-thing new.__

Flash - back,_ warm nights,_ al-most left be - hind.__

Suit - case__ of me - mo - ries,__ time af - ter...

The se - cond hand__ un - winds. If you're lost____ you can look_ and you will

find me,___ time af-ter time.___ If you fall___ I will catch you, I'll be

___ wait-ing,___ time af-ter time.___ If you're lost___ you can look_ and you will

2° Instrumental till *

___ find me,___ time af-ter time.___ If you fall___ I will catch you, I___

To Coda

___ will be wait-ing, time af-ter time.___

*

D.S. al Coda

Coda

You say,___ "Go slow"_ I fall___ be-hind.___

The se-cond hand___ un-winds._ If you're lost___ you can look_ and you will

215

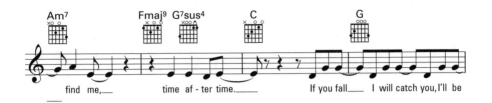

find me,—   time af - ter time.—   If you fall— I will catch you, I'll be

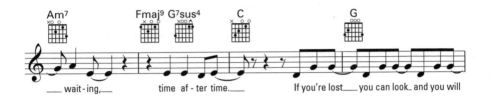

— wait - ing,—   time af - ter time.—   If you're lost— you can look— and you will

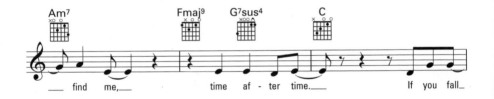

— find   me,—   time   af - ter   time.—   If   you   fall—

— I will catch— you, I— will be wait - ing,   time af - ter time.—

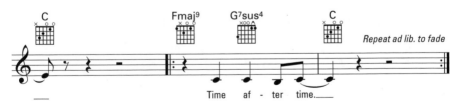

Repeat ad lib. to fade

—   Time   af - ter   time.—

Verse 2:
Sometimes you picture me
I'm walking too far ahead
You're calling to me
I can't hear what you've said
Then you say, "Go slow." I fall behind
Suitcases of memories
Time after time.

Verse 3:
After my picture fades
And darkness has turned to grey
Watching through windows
You're wondering if I'm O.K.
Secrets stolen from deep inside
Suitcases of memories
The drum beats out of time.

Tired Of Being Alone

Words & Music by Al Green

I'm so tired___ of be-ing a-lone, I'm so tired___ I'm so a-lone, won't you help ___ me, girl,___ just as soon___ as you can?___

1. Peo - ple say___ that I found a way to make you say___ that you love___ me.
(Verse 2 see block lyrics)

You did - n't go for that, it's a nat - 'ral fact, that I wan-na come back;

show me where it's at,___ Ba - by. I'm so tired ___

Repeat ad lib. and fade

Verse 2:
I guess you know that I love you so
Even though you don't want me no more
Now I'm cryin' tears, all through the years
I'll tell you like it is love me if you will.

217

Try A Little Tenderness

Words & Music by Harry Woods, Jimmy Campbell & Reg Connelly

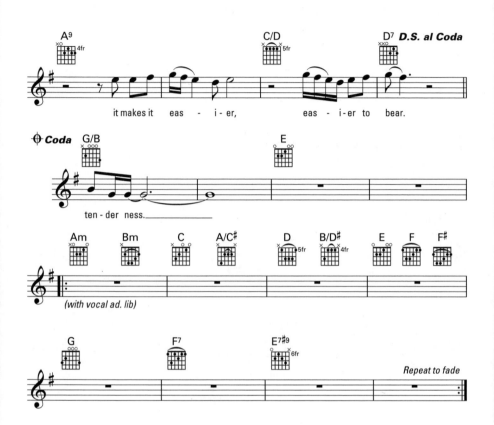

it makes it eas - i - er, eas - i - er to bear.

ten - der ness._____

(with vocal ad. lib)

Repeat to fade

Verse 3
You won't regret it
Young girls they don't forget it
Love is their only happiness
But it's all so easy
All you got to do is try a little tenderness.

Turn It On Again

Words & Music by Tony Banks, Phil Collins & Mike Rutherford

Original key: B. To match original recording, use a capo, 1st fret.

221

Verse 2:
Can't you do anything for me?
Can I touch you for a while?
Can I meet you on another day
And we will fly away?

Twist And Shout

All things considered 'Twist And Shout' was an unlikely success, having first been insipidly recorded as a calypso-flavoured song in 1962 by The Top Notes in a session overseen by the young Phil Spector. It gained more attention as a soul/rock cover by The Isley Brothers in the same year. Neither recording, however, would be as famous as yet another version, this time by The Beatles who added it to their first album's mix of original Beatle songs and personal pop favourites penned by songwriters such as Burt Bacharach, Arthur Alexander and Gerry Goffin/Carole King. 'Twist And Shout' was written by the less well-known team of Phil Medley and Bert Russell (the latter was also the co-author of 'Piece Of My Heart' so memorably sung by Erma Franklin in 1967 and Janis Joplin in 1968). Lennon's rasping vocal made 'Twist And Shout' an early rabble-rousing favourite in The Beatles' act, and the song also lent its name to a Beatles' EP extracted from their first album.

John Lennon

Twist And Shout

Words & Music by Bert Russell & Phil Medley

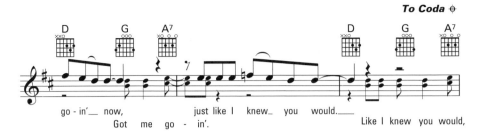

To Coda ⊕

go - in'___ now,   just like I knew___ you would.
Got   me   go - in'.   Like I knew you would,

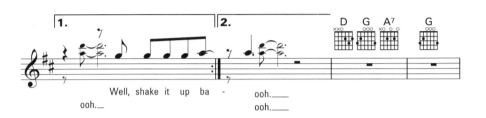

1.
2.

Well, shake it up ba -   ooh.___
ooh.___   ooh.___

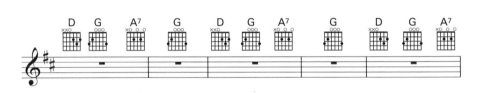

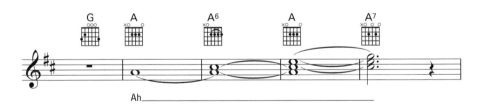

Ah_____

Whoa,   yeah._____
Ah,   yeah.___   Well,   shake   it   up   ba-

D.S. al Coda
no repeats

227

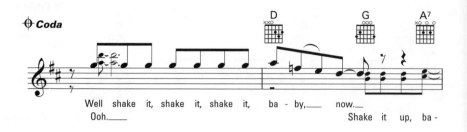

Well shake it, shake it, shake it, ba - by,___ now.___
Ooh.___ Shake it up, ba-

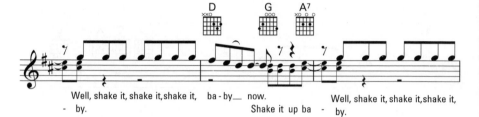

Well, shake it, shake it, shake it, ba - by___ now.
- by. Shake it up ba - by.
Well, shake it, shake it, shake it,

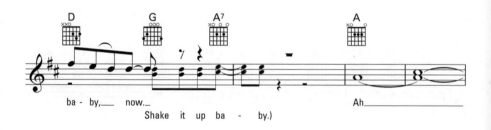

ba - by,___ now.___ Ah___
Shake it up ba - by.)

Verse 2:
You know you twist little girl (Twist little girl)
You know you twist so fine (Twist so fine)
Come on and twist a little closer now (Twist a little closer)
And let me know that you're mine (Let me know you're mine.)

Up The Junction

Words & Music by Chris Difford & Glen Tilbrook

♩ = 122

1. I nev-er thought it would hap - pen with me and a girl from
(Verse 2 see block lyrics)
Clap-ham out on the win-dy com-mon, that night I ain't for-got-ten. When she dealt out the
rat-ions with some or oth-er pas-sions, I said,"You are a la-dy," "Per-haps," she said
1. "I may be."
2.
3. I got a job with Stan-ley, he said I'd come in han-dy, and start-ed me on
Mon-day, so I had a bath on Sun-day. I worked el-e-ven hou-rs and bought the girl some

229

flow- ers. She said she'd seen a doc- tor, and noth- ing now could stop her.____

I worked all through the win- ter, the weath- er brass and bit- ter. I put a-way a

ten- ner each week to make her bet- ter. And when the time was read-y we had to sell the

tel- ly, make eve-nings by the fi-re and lit-tle kicks in-side her.____

4. This morn-ing at four- fif- ty, I took her rath-er nif- ty, down to an in-cu-

-bat- or. 'Bout thir-ty min-utes lat-er, she gave birth to a daugh-ter, with-in a year a

walk- er. She looked just like her moth- er, if there could be an-oth-er.____

5. And now she's two years old - er, her moth - er's with a
(Verse 6 see block lyrics)
sol - dier. She left me when my drink - ing, be - came a pro - per
sting - ing. The dev - il came and took me, from bar to street to
book - ie, no more nights by the tel - ly. No more nights nap - pie
smell - ing.

1.   **2.**

Verse 2:
We moved into a basement
With thoughts of our engagement
We stayed in by the telly
Although the room was smelly
We spent our time just kissing
The Railway Arms were missing
But love had got us hooked up
And all our time, it took up.

Verse 6:
Alone here in the kitchen
I feel there's something missing
I'd beg for some forgiveness
But begging's not my business
And she won't write a letter
Although I always tell her
And so it's my assumption
I'm really up the junction.

Up Where We Belong

Words & Music by Jack Nitzsche, Will Jennings & Buffy Sainte-Marie

1. Who knows what to-mor-row brings;_____ in a
(Verse 2 see block lyrics)

world, few hearts sur-vive? All I know is the way I feel; when it's

real, I keep it a-live.___ The road is__ long. There are

moun-tains in our__ way,___ but we climb a step ev-'ry day.

Love lift us up where we be-long,__ where the ea-gles cry__ on a moun-tain high.

Love lift us up where we be-long,__ far from the world be-low;__ up where the

Verse 2:
Some hang on to "used to be"
Live their lives looking behind
All we have is here and now
All our life, out there to find.

233

Vienna

Words & Music by Midge Ure, Billy Currie, Warren Cann & Christopher Allen

1.We walked in the cold air.___
(Verse 2 see block lyrics)

Freez-ing breath on a win-dow pane. Ly - ing and wait - ing.___

A man in the dark in a pic - ture frame. So

mys - tic and soul - ful.___

voice reach-ing out and a pierc - ing cry. It stays with you un - til___

the feel-ing is gone, on - ly you and I. It means

234

noth-ing to me. This means noth-ing to me,_____

oh,_____ Vi - en - na._____

2. The

This means noth-ing to me. This means

noth-ing to me,_____ oh,_____ Vi - en - na._____

Verse 2:
The music is weaving
Haunting notes, pizzicato strings; the rhythm is calling
Alone in the night as the daylight brings a cool empty silence
The warmth of your hand and a cold grey sky; it fades to the distance
The image has gone, only you and I; it means nothing to me
This means nothing to me. Oh, Vienna.

Virginia Plain

Words & Music by Bryan Ferry

1. Make me a deal___ and make it straight,___ all signed and sealed,___
(Verses 3 & 5 see block lyrics)

___ I'll take it. To Rob-ert E. Lee___ I'll show_ it,

I hope and pray___ he don't blow it,'cause we've been a - round___

___ a long_ time, just try - try - try___ try tryin' to make make the big___ time…

To Coda ⊕

2. Take me on a rol - ler coas - ter, take me for an
(Verse 4 see block lyrics)

air-plane ride.___ Take me for a six day won - der,___ but don't you,

don't you throw my pride a - side,__ be - sides, what's real and make__ be - lieve. Ba - by Jane's in A - ca - pul - co, we're all fly - ing down to Ri - o.__

1.

N.C.

2.

D.C. al Coda

__ 3. Throw me a line__ got to reach for some - thing new.

☩ *Coda*

Half spoken: What's her name, Vir - gin - i - a Plain.

Verse 3:

Throw me a line I'm sinking fast, clutching at straws can't make it
Havana sound we're trying, hard edge the hipster jiving
Last picture shows down the drive-in, you're so sheer you're so chic
Teenage rebel of the week.

Verse 4:

Flavours of the mountain streamline, midnight blue casino floors
Dance the cha-cha through till sunrise, opens up exclusive doors, oh wow!
Just like flamingoes look the same so, me and you, just we two
Got to search for something new.

Verse 5:

Far beyond the pale horizon, some place near the desert strand
Where my Studebaker takes me, that's where I'll make my stand but wait
Can't you see that Holzermane, what's her name
Virginia Plain.

Waiting In Vain

Words & Music by Bob Marley

239

Verse 2:
It's been three years since I'm knockin' on your door
And I still can knock some more
Ooh girl, ooh girl, is it feasible
I wanna know now, for I to know some more?
Ya see, in life I know there is lots of grief
But your love is my relief
Tears in my eyes burn, tears in my eyes burn
While I'm waiting, while I'm waiting for my turn.

Walk On By

Words by Hal David • Music by Burt Bacharach

1. If you see me walk-ing down the street, and I start to cry___ each time we meet,
(Verse 2 see block lyrics)

walk on by,___ walk on___ by.

Make be-lieve___ that you don't see the tears; just let me grieve___ in

pri-vate,'cause each time that I see you___ I break down and cry. Walk on by,

___ walk on by,___ just walk on by.___

1.

2. 'Cause ___ Just walk on by.___

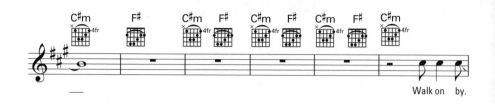

Walk on by.

Walk on by._____ Fool-ish pride___ is

all that I have left, so let me hide___ these tears and___ all the sad-ness_ that you

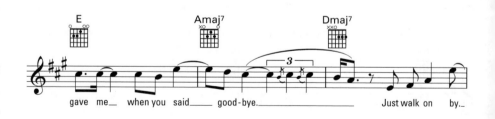

gave me_ when you said___ good-bye._____ Just walk on by._

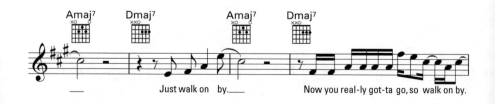

Just walk on by.___ Now you real-ly got-ta go, so walk on by.

242

Said you real-ly got-ta go, so walk on by.____

Ba - by leave, you'll nev - er see the tears_ I cry.____

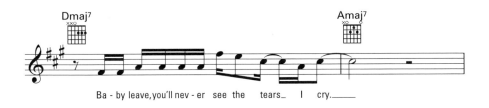

Ba - by leave, you'll nev - er see the tears_ I cry.____

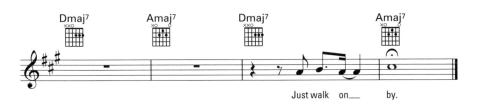

Just walk on__ by.

Verse 2:
I just can't get over losing you
And if I seem broken and blue
Walk on by, walk on by
Foolish pride is all that I have left
So let me hide the tears of all the sadness
That you gave me when you said goodbye
You walked on by, you walked on by, just walk on by.

Wake Up Little Susie

Words & Music by Felice & Boudleaux Bryant

Wake up, lit - tle Su - sie,___ wake up.

Wake up, lit - tle Su - sie,___ wake up.

1. We've both been sound a - sleep,___ wake up,___ lit - tle Su - sie, and
(Verse 2 see block lyrics)

weep. The mov - ie's ov - er, it's four o' - clock_ and we're in trou - ble

deep. Wake up,___ lit - tle Su - sie, wake up,___ lit - tle Su - sie,___

well, what are we gon - na tell your Ma - ma?___

244

What are we gon-na tell your Pa?____ What are we gon-na tell our friends

____ when they say, "Ooh la la". Wake up,____ lit-tle Su - sie____

wake up,____ lit-tle Su - sie.____ Well, we told your Ma-ma that

we'd be in by ten. Well, Su-sie ba - by, looks like we goofed a - gain.____

____ Wake up,____ lit-tle Su - sie,____ wake up,____ lit-tle Su - sie,____

we've got - ta go home.

Su - sie.____

Verse 2:
The movie wasn't so hot
It didn't have much of a plot
We fell asleep, our goose is cooked
Our reputation is shot.

Way Down

Words & Music by Layng Martine Jr.

1. Babe, you're get - tin' clos - er, the lights are go - in' dim.

(Verse 2 see block lyrics)

The sound of your breath - in' has made the mood I'm in.

All of my re - sis - tance is ly - in' on the floor,

you're tak - ing me to plac - es that I'm nev-er been be - fore.

Oo! And I can feel it, feel it,

feel it, feel it.

Way down where the mu - sic plays,

(Way down!)

(Way

246

way down like a ti - dal wave.___ Way down where the
down!) (Way down!)

fires___ blaze, way down,___

To Coda ⊕

down,___ way, way on down.
(Way on

down.)

Hold me a-gain as tight

D.S. al Coda

___ as you can, I need you so. Ba - by, let's go!

⊕ **Coda**

down way on down.)

Verse 2:
Ooh, my head is spinning
You got me in your spell
A hundred magic fingers
On a swirling carousel
The medicine within me
No doctor could prescribe
Your love is doing something
That I just can't describe.

We Are Family

Words & Music by Bernard Edwards & Nile Rodgers

- ple a - round us, they say___ "Can they be___ that close?"

Just let me state for the re - cord,___

we're giv - ing love in a fam - 'ly dose.

We are fa - mi - ly, I got all my sis - ters with me.___

___ We are fa - mi - ly,

get up ev - 'ry - bo - dy and sing.___

Repeat to fade

Verse 2:
Living life is fun and we've just begun
To get our share of this world's delights
(High) High hopes we have for the future
And our goal's in sight
(We) No, we don't get depressed
Here's what we call our golden rule
Have faith in you and the things you do
You won't go wrong, oh no, this is our family jewel.

What's Love Got To Do With It

Words & Music by Graham Lyle & Terry Britten

1. You must un - der - stand that the touch of__your hand makes my pulse re - act;__
(Verse 2 see block lyrics)

that it's on - ly__ the thrill of boy meet-ing girl;__ op-po - sites at - tract. It's

phy-si - cal,__ on-ly lo - gi - cal,_____ you must try to__ ig-nore that it

means more__than that. Oh,_____ what's love__ got to do,__ got to do__with it? What's love__ but a

se-cond hand e - mo - tion?__ What's love__ got to do,__ got to do__with it?

Who needs a heart when a heart can be bro - ken? 2. It heart can be bro - ken.__

250

Verse 2:

It may seem to you
That I'm acting confused
When you're close to me
If I tend to look dazed
I read it some place
I've got cause to be

There's a name for it
There's a phrase that fits
But whatever the reason
You do it for me.

251

With Or Without You

A major stepping stone in the career of U2 'With Or Without You' was a single taken from the band's big 1987 album, *The Joshua Tree*. Produced by Daniel Lanois and Brian Eno it reached No. 1 in the US and enjoyed success in many international charts. All of the hallmarks of the U2 sound can be heard in this song, with The Edge's atmospheric guitar textures to the fore. If not exactly a U2 signature tune, 'With Or Without You' is one of the band's most frequently performed and often covered songs. Bono credits Scott Walker's 1983 album *Climate Of The Hunter* as an influence in its composition.

Bono

With Or Without You

Words & Music by U2

See the stone___ set in your eyes,___ see the thorn___ twist in your side,___ I wait___ for you.___

1. Sleight of hand___ and twist of fate,___ on a bed of nails___
(Verse 2 see block lyrics)
___ she makes me wait___ and I wait___ with - out___ you.___ With or with - out___ you,___

1.
with or with - out___ you.

Verse 2:
Through the storm we reach the shore
You give it all but I want more
And I'm waiting for you.

Why Does It Always Rain On Me?

Words & Music by Fran Healy

Verse 2:
I can't stand myself
I'm being held up by invisible men
Still life on a shelf when
I got my mind on something else.

You Never Can Tell

Words & Music by Chuck Berry

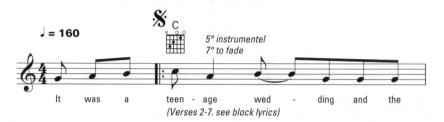

♩ = 160

5° instrumentel
7° to fade

It was a teen - age wed - ding and the

(Verses 2-7. see block lyrics)

old folks wished 'em well___ you could see___

___ that Pi - erre___ did tru - ly love the ma - de - moi - selle___

G7

___ and now the young m'- sieur___ and ma - dame___

___ have rung the cha - pel bell___ c'est la vie,___

say the old___ folks, they go to show you nev - er can

C

1-6. **7**

D.S. *to fade*

tell._____ 2. They fur-nished

Verse 2:
They furnished off an apartment with a two-room Roebuck sale
The Coolerator was crammed with TV dinners and ginger ale
But when Pierre found work, the little money come in worked out well
C'est la vie, say the old folks, they go to show you never can tell.

Verse 3:
They had a hi-fi phono, boy did they let it blast
Seven hundred little records all rockin' rhythm and jazz
But when the sun went down the rapid tipple of the music fell
C'est la vie, say the old folks, they go to show you never can tell.

Verse 4:
They bought a souped-up Jitney was a cherry-red '53
And drove it down to Orleans to celebrate the anniversary
It was there where Pierre was wedded to the lovely madamoiselle
C'est la vie, say the old folks, they go to show you never can tell.

Verse 5:
Instrumental

Verse 6:
They had a teenage wedding and the old folks wished them well
You could see that Pierre did truly love the Mademoiselle
And now the young M'sieur and Madame have rung the chapel bell
C'est la vie, say the old folks, they go to show you never can tell.

Verse 7:
Instrumental to fade

Your Song

Words & Music by Elton John & Bernie Taupin

1. It's a lit-tle bit fun-ny this feel-ing in-

(Verses 2-4 see block lyrics)

side._____ I'm not one of those_____ who can

ea - si - ly hide._____ I don't have much

mo-ney_____ but,__ boy, if I_____ did._____ I'd buy a big

1.

house where__ we both__ could live.

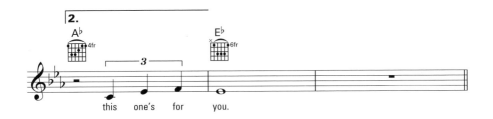

2.

A♭   E♭

this one's for you.

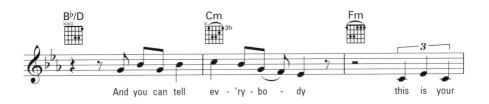

B♭/D   Cm   Fm

And you can tell ev - 'ry - bo - dy   this is your

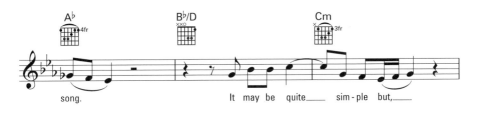

A♭   B♭/D   Cm

song.   It may be quite___ sim - ple but,___

Fm   A♭   Cm

now that it's done.___   I hope you don't mind,

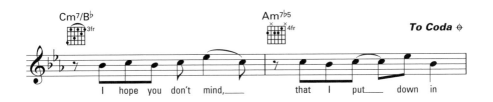

Cm7/B♭   Am7♭5   **To Coda ⊕**

I hope you don't mind,___   that I put___ down in

263

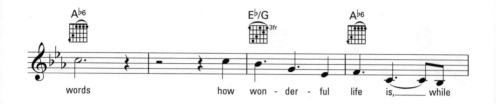

words   how won - der - ful life is,____ while

D.C. al Coda *(with repeats)*

you're__ in the world.____

♦ *Coda*

words   how won - der - ful

life is,____ when you're in the world.__

I hope you don't mind, I hope you don't mind,__ that I put__ down in

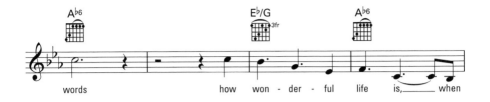

words   how   won - der - ful   life   is,_____ when

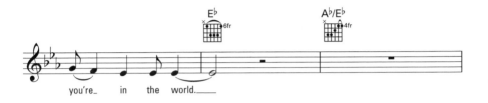

you're_   in   the   world._____

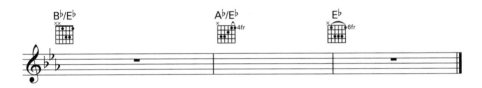

Verse 2:
If I was a sculptor but then again no
Or a man who makes potions in a travelling show
I know it's not much but it's the best I can do
My gift is my song yeah, this one's for you.

Verse 3:
I sat on the roof and kicked off the moss
Well a few of the verses, well, they've got me quite cross
But the sun's been quite kind while I wrote this song
It's for people like you that keep it turned on.

Verse 4:
So excuse me forgetting but these things I do
You see I've forgotten if they're green or they're blue
Anyway the thing is what I really mean
Yours are the sweetest eyes I've ever seen.

You're Gorgeous

Words & Music by Stephen Jones

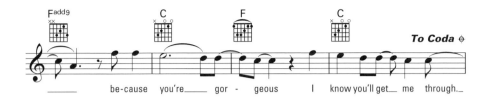

be-cause you're___ gor - geous I know you'll get__ me through.__

3 & 4° Vocal ad lib.

⊕ Coda

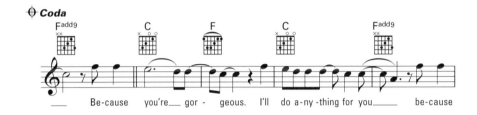

___ Be-cause you're__ gor - geous. I'll do a-ny-thing for you___ be-cause

you're___ gor - geous I know you'll get__ me,__ know you'll get__ me through.__

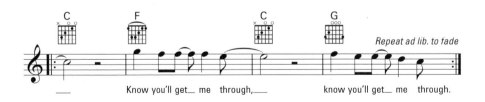

___ Know you'll get__ me through,___ know you'll get__ me through.

Verse 3:
You said my clothes were sexy
You tore away my shirt
You rubbed an ice cube on my chest
Snapped me till it hurt.

Verse 4:
You said I wasn't cheap
You paid me twenty pounds
You promised to put me in a magazine
On every table, in every lounge.

267

You're So Vain

Words & Music by Carly Simon

♩ = 105

Am⁷

1. You walked in to the par - ty like you were
(Verses 2 & 4 see block lyrics)

F   Am⁷

walk-ing on-to___ a yacht;___ your hat stra - te-gic-'lly dipped be - low

F   Am⁷

___ one eye, your scarf, it was a - pri - cot.___ You had

F   G   Em⁷   Am⁷   F

one eye in the mir - ror as___ you watched your-self___ ga - votte,

C   G   F

___ and___ all the girls___dreamed that they'd___ be your part - ner, they'd___

C

___ be your part - ner and you're___ so___ vain,___ you

268

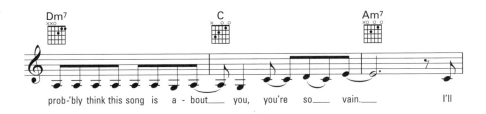

prob-'bly think this song is a - bout___ you, you're so___ vain.___ I'll

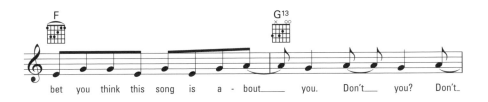

bet you think this song is a - bout___ you. Don't___ you? Don't___

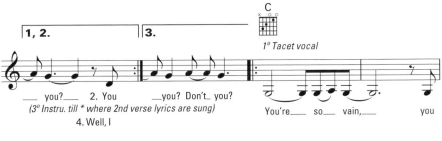

___ you?___ 2. You ___you? Don't___ you?
*(3º Instru. till * where 2nd verse lyrics are sung)*
4. Well, I

You're___ so___ vain,___ you

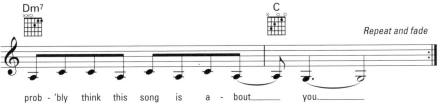

Repeat and fade

prob - 'bly think this song is a - bout___ you.___

Verse 2:
You had me several years ago
When I was still quite naïve
Well, you said that we made such a pretty pair
And that you would never leave
But you gave away the things you loved
And one of them was me
I had some dreams there were clouds in my coffee
Clouds in my coffee and you're so vain *etc.*

Verse 4:
Well, I hear you went up to Saratoga
And your horse nat'rally won
Then you flew your Learjet up to Nova Scotia
To see the total eclipse of the sun
Well, you're where you should be all the time
And when you're not you're with some underworld spy
Or the wife of a close friend
Wife of a close friend and you're so vain *etc.*

You Do Something To Me

Words & Music by Paul Weller

1. You do___ some-thing to me, ___ some-thing___ deep in - side, ___ I'm hang-ing on___ the wi - re___ for a love_ I'll nev - er find.___ 2. You do___ some-thing_ ___ won - der - ful___ then chase_ it all___ a - way, ___ ___ mix-ing my__ e - mo - tions,

that throws_ me back_ a - gain._

Hang-ing on the wi - re, yeah,_

I'm wait-ing for my change,_ I'm danc-ing_ through the

fi - re_ just to catch a flame and feel real a - gain.

1.

2.

You do_ some - thing

to me,_ some-where_deep in _ side._

I'm hop - ing_ to get close to_

271